Praise fo

"*Along Came a Stroke* is a beautiful memoir. . . . Haas gives advice to her readers about what to do and what not to do during the different phases of a stroke and recovery. . . . I also enjoyed the humor that Haas brought to the table despite the serious subject. . . . It's is a wonderful book that people of all ages can learn from."

—Portland Book Review (five stars)

"Fascinating and informative, entertaining and easy to read. I felt as if Haas was telling me everything over a cup of coffee. I breezed through this book and recommend it to not just stroke survivors but anyone who reads."

—Josephine Carr, former hospital manager,
Bradenton, Florida

"Wonderful to read . . . straightforward and easy-to-digest . . . packed with helpful information and tidbits. Even able-bodied folks will find things that are personally valuable and applicable to their own lives. Whether Haas did it on purpose or not, this is a book about deliberate practice and stroke survivors will find it a revelation."

—Szifra Birke, executive consultant,
Lowell, Massachusetts

"This book would hold anyone's attention, whether they had a stroke or not. The author is very articulate and it's easy to read . . . at times quite gripping."

—Lisa Bruce, Berkeley, California

ALONG CAME A STROKE

ALONG CAME A STROKE

My Story of Survival and Recovery

Eileen Haas

**BOLD
STORY
PRESS**

Washington, DC

Bold Story Press, Washington, DC 20016
www.boldstorypress.com

Copyright © 2022 by Eileen Haas

This book is a memoir and it reflects the author's present
recollections of experiences over time.

First edition published October 2022

Library of Congress Control Number: 2021922587

ISBN: 978-1-954805-18-7 (paperback)
ISBN: 978-1-954805-19-4 (e-book)

Text and cover design by Laurie Entringer
Cover photo by Johny Goerend
Author photo by Josephine Carr

Printed in the United States of America
10 9 8 7 6 5 4 3 2 1

To stroke survivors everywhere.

You are heroes, all.

CONTENTS

PART ONE

PART TWO

CONTENTS

PART THREE

PART FOUR

CONTENTS

PART FIVE

PART SIX

CONTENTS

PART SEVEN

PART ONE

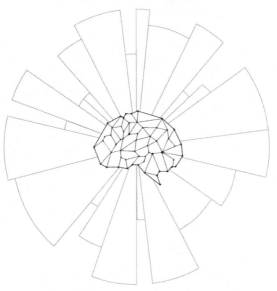

SUDDENLY,

A

STROKE

I was folding laundry.
I don't think you can get any more mundane. Dusting, maybe, or melting butter in a pan. I'm sure you can think of a hundred things, but the point is the same: I wasn't doing anything special.

Suddenly, I couldn't see. A zipper zipped up in my left field of vision, complete with sound effects. *Ziiippp.* Like on a pair of jeans. I knew I was in big, big trouble.

I felt something warm release at the back of my head and cascade down my spine. I'm having a stroke, I thought. *That must be blood.*

Even now, I'm amazed at my presence of mind. I could have just fallen apart. I could have just died. But I sprang into action instead.

You know those silly things people send you on the Internet? What to do in case of heart attack, stroke, or stomach pains. Well, I actually read them. And remember, it seems.

You always wonder how you're going to react when *The Moment* comes. Don't think you'll just fold up shop and go away. You won't. I was having a stroke. And, because of one of those emails I got, and skimmed, I knew I had to get help right away.

But first, I had to make some decisions. Big ones. Should I live or should I die? It's a powerful thing, having death in

3

your hands. I felt anything but powerful at the time. Powerless is how I felt.

And determined. Should I live or should I die? I was old enough to die, in my estimation. Yet I had decades left, and I felt unfinished. My story hadn't been completed yet. All of this in a fraction of a second, mind you. That's another thing—you think *fast*.

They say your life flashes before your eyes when you're dying. Mine didn't flash before me, but I did contemplate death. And I decided not to die (obviously, or I wouldn't be writing this). Eventually I would die, of course, but I wasn't ready. I wasn't done having adventures, that was for sure. That was right, because I'm having quite an adventure recovering.

All this went through my head in about two seconds. I was still sitting on the bench at the end of my bed. The laundry was half-folded; the basket at my feet. I knew I had to get to a phone, or I'd be toast. This involved crossing the bed. Piece of cake, you think. It wasn't.

It was miles across that bed to the phone on my night table. I was dizzy. So dizzy I didn't want to move. So dizzy that the slightest motion brought on waves of nausea. Yet I had to get to that phone.

They say, in a life-and-death situation, you can do amazing things, like lift a car, because of the adrenaline pumping through your body. I must have been filled with adrenaline, because somehow I crossed those miles of white sheets. I might as well have been crossing an ocean in a rowboat. Every inch was something I had to fight for, but fight I did.

From the time you can understand what a telephone is, it's drilled into your head to dial 911 in an emergency. But you have to have the presence of mind to do it, and you have to remember the number as the life is leaving your body. This is easier said than done.

I remembered one phone number, and it wasn't 911. It was the cell phone number of a friend who lived up the street. I only had it in me to dial that one number. This is the most worrisome thing about having something like a stroke happen when you're alone and can't depend on someone else to have a clear head and a good memory. There's just nothing to be done about it.

Miraculously, my neighbor answered. She never answered! She started asking me questions, so in spite of my dizziness, my nausea, my feeling that a trip across the bed was like a trip across an ocean, I said simply, "I'm dying here." I heard her boyfriend shouting in the background. "Get over there!" Later, I knew he would have come running, but, being in a wheelchair, he couldn't.

I was dying, and I knew it. Somehow, I'd gone from a healthy, vibrant, well-exercised woman to this creature who couldn't walk across a room to pick up a phone. I started to throw up. The nausea had finally culminated in the inevitable.

Next thing I knew, I heard my friend and neighbor's key in the door. Simultaneously, I heard the whine of a siren. For once, it was for me. I can't begin to tell you how grateful I felt. Those people, the paramedics, are trained and they know what to do. Do they realize how important they are? I hope so.

I heard people clomping up the stairs. It turned out to be two young guys, moving very, very fast. Their faces told me everything I needed to know. One of them crouched down (I was on the floor at this point and could not move), and shone a light into my eyes. I knew he was looking at my pupils. I knew they weren't the same.

I looked at his face. *Holy moly*, it seemed to say. *This is the real deal. No kidding around.* I went in and out of consciousness. I remember the paramedics (who were those guys? I want to thank them) carrying me down my long, curving staircase in a sling. Sun on my face. I remember being put in an ambulance. I remember the paramedic saying to me, over and over, *Stay with me. Just stay with me.*

I don't recall anything else until a couple of days later.

IN THE
ICU

I was isolated in the ICU. My brothers were there. I thought, *This must be bad if both my brothers flew in.* They looked scared and helpless. I later learned how many decisions they had made. They tell you to have a DNR. If I had had one, I would not be here writing this book. I knew my brothers were the types to never give up hope. To do whatever it takes. They must have told the surgeons this. They don't talk about it, but I can hear their voices saying, *Save our sister.*

What exactly happened to me? Did I have an aneurysm that burst? Did a blood vessel give out? Doctors aren't sure, and to this day they'll argue about it. I know I had a hemorrhagic stroke, not an ischemic stroke.* This is important somehow, but to my way of thinking, if you've had a stroke, you've had a stroke. You're messed up.

Whatever happened to me was so mysterious and rare that my neurosurgeon flew in a specialist from Washington, DC, to consult with him. I only know this because the specialist they flew in told me. Sometime and somewhere,

---

*There are two kinds of strokes, as if you didn't know. An ischemic stroke is caused by very high blood pressure. A hemorrhagic stroke is a brain bleed, caused by a burst blood vessel or ruptured aneurysm. Both are bad news.

after I regained consciousness. *Those doctors saved my life.*

I woke up in the ICU. I had a catheter and an IV drip. Containing what (the IV drip), I don't know. I was groggy. I was unpleasant to be around. The back of my head was shaved. To this day, I don't know what the surgeon did back there, and I don't want to. My hair, which has all grown back, covers it anyway.

They must have given me good drugs, because I was hallucinating like crazy. A woman gave birth alone except for her mother in the next cubicle, curtains drawn. I don't think so! There was a small blonde who prayed with me. Maybe she was real. My brothers spoke to me. I have no idea what they said. I probably answered, but I have no idea what I said, either.

It was a shadowy time.

In the Rehab Hospital

If I remember little about the ICU, I remember a lot more about the rehab hospital, because I was there for five weeks. The nurses kindly showed me how to lock my valuables away (someone brought my purse from the hospital), and where to hide the key.

I was still at the stage where I was saying to myself, *I had a stroke? Not me!* The whole thing seemed preposterous. The fact that I couldn't walk or use my right hand, that my voice was degenerating, that I shook all over on my right side, and the back of my head was shaved—all were things I waved off as temporary. Surely they would go away in a few days. (They do, for some lucky people. Not for me, and not for lots of stroke survivors).

Friends and family came to visit every day. Although I was sleeping a lot, I always roused myself for these visits. They were precious, and I was not about to waste them. Still, I found myself thinking, *Why is everybody acting as though I'm permanently damaged?*

I didn't know it at the time, but I was in the first stage of grief—denial. Having a stroke is not like getting a head cold. You may get over it, but you'll always know you had a stroke. As a friend put it, it's a "life-changing event." For better or worse, you'll never be the same.

At the rehab hospital, the chocolate bars piled up. That

should have been my first clue about changes happening right then and there, but I was too out of it to make the connection. Everyone brought me dark chocolate because they knew how much I loved it, but I actually wasn't interested. The nurses must have had a good time, because I gave all of the chocolate to them.

Clue number two: I ate the rehab hospital food without complaining. It must have been awful, but everything tasted like cardboard anyway. I ate dutifully, to stay alive. When I got the little piece of paper every afternoon giving me breakfast choices, I randomly circled things and promptly forgot them. So each breakfast in the cafeteria was a surprise. Oh, did I order orange juice? I don't remember doing that, but okay, I'll drink it.

It took me a while, several months actually (after I'd been home for a bit), to enter the anger stage of grief. I couldn't do anything right. Why was that? I wasn't getting better fast enough. What in the world was going on? I kept asking my caregivers when I would be "normal." Truthfully, I would never be normal again, but if they'd told me that, I would have flipped out. It's better that I didn't know.

The only one who told me the unvarnished truth was my home caregiver Delia. No bromides from her. Putting the worst possible scenario together, she told me I'd always need someone to take care of me. I did not respond well to that. It was true at the time she told me, but by year three I was doing most things myself. It's only improved from there, but I can still hear her saying, "You're not out of the woods yet." I think I'm now well out of the woods, but I'm still wandering in some sort of forest.

The next stage of grief, bargaining, came for me in the form of rewards. "If you climb three rungs of the ladder, you can read ten pages of your book." It worked—I must have really wanted to read that book! I climbed three rungs of that ladder, even though I had butterflies in my stomach at rung two.

I knew enough not to ask for getting well completely, but I broke my healing down into smaller victories. Carrying a glass of water from the fridge to the living room table. Making the bed up with fresh sheets. And yes, I'm almost ashamed to admit it, but doing a laundry was a source of triumph. It was hard at first, but I bargained over that one, too. When the laundry was done and put away, I celebrated with a piece of cake (my appetite—and sweet tooth—had come back by then).

Stage four, acceptance, was and still is the hardest stage of grief. I think I accepted that my life had changed irrevocably around year five (and five years is a long time), but I never fully accepted having had a stroke. I stopped denying it, but I'm still striving to be more normal. I've had moments—just moments—when I feel absolutely recovered, but those are very few and far between. However, they give me lots of hope and remind me what my goal is.

Around year four, I met a woman at a party who'd had an ischemic stroke ten years prior to my meeting her. She seemed fine, but I've learned that *seeming* anything is to be taken with a big grain of salt. She talked at length about her stroke, which should have told me something. Mentioning the stroke was understandable, but going on and on about it wasn't. I've come to realize that you never forget having a stroke. It's that big.

When I got to the acceptance stage, I was well on my journey. Admitting that I had a stroke was a big step. It allowed me to step out of the looking glass and come to terms with what I'd been left with and what I could do about it.

THE "D" WORD

There. I've said it. It has to be the most unpopular subject you could ever bring up. Yet it is going to happen to everybody. No exceptions.

You know I'm talking about death, right? Bear with me, because I assure you this is not going to be a downer. On the contrary, it's going to be quite upbeat.

I had a near-death experience. Did you? There should be a special club for people like us, because nobody else understands it.

Recently I had lunch with a cousin. "You almost died," she said in awe. That's the reaction you get. In fact, if you were on the healthy and untouched side of it, you'd probably feel the same way and say the same things.

Everyone has something they proselytize about. For me, it's death. People are so frightened of it. Everything ends! Life ends! But I'm here to tell you that death is *nothing to be frightened of*. In my experience, it's quite wonderful, in fact.

I didn't go through any tunnels, or see a white light. *I did* experience the most profound sense of peace you can ever imagine. I take that back, because you can't really imagine it. *I* can't imagine it. *I* can't conjure it up. It is a letting go that, on a scale of one to ten, is a twenty. You don't care about anything, and I mean anything.

You happily leave it up to the living to figure things out. No one is going to ask *you* anymore. For the first time in your existence, people will leave you alone.

And . . . you feel so wonderful, you lose the fear that has haunted you all your life, whatever that fear happens to be. You realize that when it truly comes, death will be a blessing.

Think of it—when a child is born, when there's that slap and cry—everybody celebrates. Even though there are probably a great many trials and tribulations awaiting that child. At times, life may become unbearable to her. Yet we're so happy! When someone dies, on the other hand, people speak in hushed tones, and they are sad and depressed. What's there to be depressed about? That person just got released! (In my humble opinion.)

It doesn't do much good to talk about it. Yet if my stroke (or someone's heart attack, accident, whatever) has done anything permanent, it's taken away that fear of death. I may live into my 90s, but I hope I never forget that death is my best friend, not my enemy.

As I lay there in the ICU, and my brothers congratulate me on staying alive, I think fondly about death, and I'm not a morbid person. It just *felt so good* to step over that line. I'm here to tell you, death is nothing to be afraid of.

BREAKFAST
WITH
IDIOTS

I am having breakfast in a room full of idiots. Some are drooling into their yogurt. Others are scarfing down eggs and bacon. An attendant, who must be assigned to me because she always pushes my wheelchair, coaxes me to eat.

"Have some more," she urges as she pushes the *Special K* towards me. *You must be kidding*, I think as I obediently eat another spoonful.

I look around the breakfast room at my fellow stroke survivors. All wear the same stupefied expression. *How in the world did I get here*, their expressions seem to say. I couldn't possibly be one of them, could I? The men look angry. The women look confused. They are all ages, from all walks of life. Just last week they probably were artists, teachers, carpenters. This week they are—what, exactly? A group of idiots?

I remember one man—dark-haired, mid-forties, mad at the world. He swept his entire tray off the table with a crash, and informed the entire room that he was going home later. Because this place was *terrible*. A young woman was sitting in the corner, staring at the things in front of her—milk, cereal, a banana, concentrating hard and trying to figure out what she was supposed to do with them. She was so pretty. And part of her brain had obviously been damaged.

These were my new compatriots, God help me. I hated

them at first, then developed a fond respect for them. They were survivors. They were brave, brave people.

SOME STATISTICS ABOUT STROKES

The following statistics are from our very own government, the Centers for Disease Control (CDC) to be exact.

- **Every year, more than 795,000 people in the United States have a stroke.** About 610,000 of these are "new" strokes. This is actually quite a small number, when you consider the population as a whole. You're in exclusive territory.

- **Someone has a stroke every 40 seconds.** And dies of it every 4 minutes.

- **About 185,000 strokes are in people who have already had strokes. This is almost 1 in 4! No wonder stroke makes you paranoid.** Once you have had one, chances are very good that you'll have another one. As a doctor told me, "Your circulatory system has been compromised." I like to think of it as a remembering. Your body remembers that this is a way to let off steam. I would like to see statistics on how many people have second strokes if they change their lifestyle dramatically. Something tells me that serenity staves off stroke.

- **Stroke-related costs in the U.S. between 2014-2015 were about $46 billion.** We are expensive, a whole industry unto ourselves. Maybe we wouldn't cost so much if therapists helped us recover more. And if insurance covered those costs.

- **Stroke reduces mobility in more than half of people over age 65.** If you ask me, mobility in this age group is reduced anyway. But reducing it further is . . . troubling.
- **Across all age groups, stroke is a leading cause of serious disability.** The younger you are when you have a stroke, the more of a chance you have to fully come back. Children and teenagers, for instance, are used to learning new things all the time, and will regain what they've lost quicker than older people. And, possibly, they'll regain more.
- **In 2009, 34% of people hospitalized for stroke were under the age of 65.** Although your risk of stroke increases with age, truthfully, you can have a stroke at any age. I personally know several young people who have had strokes.
- **Speed of response matters.** Stroke patients who arrive at the ER within 3 hours of their first symptoms often have less disability after 3 months than those who delayed treatment. So if your friends and/or family sit around arguing whether you're having a stroke or not, it will not help you. They can argue to their heart's content while you're being treated.

I'm going to add a few things that I know about this, courtesy of my rehab hospital.

Fetuses can have strokes *in the womb*. (Now, that is scary to contemplate.) I had none of the risk factors, I mean not one (except for stress), and I had a stroke, anyway. What does this mean? You tell me, because I don't know.

One of the people who helped me get better said that they were seeing more people with strokes than ever before. Even those, like me, with no risk factors.

How do you reconcile this with so many people now living to be 100 or more? I have an uncle who is one of these— he is now 98. My dad's brother! By the way, his wife (my lovely aunt) had a stroke in her 80s and that didn't stop her from living to 99.

I'm no expert, but I'm guessing that good medical care

plays a big role. Lesson: live near a big city with a big hospital. If you can.

Now let's get back to my story, which is a lot more engaging than these numbers.

The One
Good Thing
About
the Hospital

My bed is too hard, or too something. The mattress is thin. The blanket is inadequate. Kind of like being on an airplane, only worse. The nurses rarely come when you call them. You can sit up and watch TV, but the television doesn't work, and besides, you have to pay extra for that. On some days, it does work, but you only get two channels. News and weather, weather and news. Neither one does me any good. The news belongs to someone else, and the weather... when you never go outside, it doesn't matter. I know it is sunny and warm, but it might as well be raining. In fact, it would match my mood better.

Still, I love my bed and whatever I am out doing, I can't wait to get back to it. For me, it is Ali Baba's bed. Nothing distresses me more than the sight of a wheelchair on the side of that bed, with the attendant waiting for me to get up and get in the chair. I have to keep in mind that whatever they're going to make me do—eat, therapy exercises—my bed will be waiting at the end of it. Something good, because when you've had a stroke, you need something good in your life.

In spite of that wonderful bed, they say that when you are sick, a hospital is the last place you want to go to get better. How right they are! In fact, it is downright depressing.

This is not the fault of the surgeons, nurses, and orderlies, who often work their tails off and really care about you.

They are stymied by a system that only cares how much the executives are taking home and how big their bonuses will be. Everything is rigidly regulated, although each patient is different and what will help one may harm another.

Take the infamous middle-of-the-night vitals check. They actually do wake you up to take your blood pressure, temperature, see how much oxygen is in your blood, change your IV. This entails turning on bright fluorescent overhead lights, sending several nurses to do this in case you are recalcitrant, bustling around your bed. You are disbelieving, since it was nothing short of a miracle that you got to sleep at lights-out time to begin with. They want you *up*.

No matter that you had a stroke and are wondering how you'll get through the day ahead. They have their marching orders. In this way, we seem to have gone backward since the 21st century. It is actually torture being woken up in the middle of the night, but they still do it. They still want to know how you are at 2:30 a.m.

I think I reached a low point when it was deemed okay for me to take a shower. I didn't want it. The nurses had been threatening for days, so I knew it was coming. Now I empathize with the way the homeless feel. That dirt felt protective, and I didn't want it removed. But one afternoon I was awakened, wheeled into a "special room," handed a nozzle and a bar of soap, and told to wash myself off.

This was a hospital in Berkeley, California, but at times I felt as if I were in the London of Dickens. All that was missing was a madwoman running up and down the halls, hair and nightgown streaming, and I'm sure they had one of those, too, but I never saw her.

Somehow, in spite of the fact that the Bastille seemed friendly after this, I took a shower, using the nozzle to hose myself down. It was rather humiliating, but I was clean. My wheelchair was wet, but somehow they dried it off while I was sleeping. Or switched it with another one.

That shower was exhausting. I slept a lot, but after any activity, I was wiped.

THERAPISTS
AND
WHEELCHAIRS

In the rehab hospital, after being wheeled to breakfast with idiots, some of whom I knew quite well by then, there's a short nap. I am awakened, made to dress and get in my wheelchair, and go off to my therapy appointment.

I now know the difference between an OT (occupational therapist), a PT (physical therapist), and an ST (speech therapist). But early in rehab I didn't. I would always ask and be given a curt answer (OT or PT; ST came later). So I never knew what type of therapy awaited me.

My OT, the one responsible for my writing, couldn't do much and gave up after about three weeks. My PTs were wonderful and did the lion's share of work. Bret and Marilyn, I am so grateful to you both. All that linoleum tapping and patty-cake playing paid off. I have only good memories of both of you.

Bret pushed me way beyond what I thought I could do. Positively Machiavellian, he was an endless fount of exercises, some of which had me shaking my head. But they all had a good effect. Slowly, oh so slowly, my balance began to come back.

Marilyn worked on increasing my strength. My stroke mainly affected my right side, so with very good humor she had me doing things I hated but that brought me a little closer to normalcy. Like patty-cake. Who would ever think that a little girl's clapping game could be so effective? Yet it was.

I realized that all those games I played as a child were teaching me balance and hand-eye coordination. Silly things like taking everything out of the pantry and then putting it back teaches you organization, geometry, and memory. Ask me what was in that pantry—decades later, I still know.

But I'd already learned this stuff as a child—did I have to learn it all over again? Unfortunately, yes, I did. Because part of my brain has been wiped out. What was really worrisome was that I couldn't walk. I could make the transition from bed to wheelchair and back again (I had to practice even this at first), but beyond that my legs didn't work. I still was so dizzy that the room whirled around when I sat up in bed. The stroke wiped out my inner gyroscope, lucky me. It would be years until I could navigate with assurance again, something I thankfully didn't know at the time.

I was frightened about my legs. What if I never walked again? Lots of people spend decades in a wheelchair. Was I about to become one of them? It seemed impossible, yet I was being wheeled around everywhere. It wasn't so bad, but I knew at some point it would be.

I had mixed feelings about that wheelchair. On the one hand, it was a comfort, and it was surprisingly nice to be wheeled around everywhere. I was grateful, oh so grateful, to have it by my bed at all times.

On the other hand, it was a symbol of failure. All my life I've been walking everywhere, and I love to walk. Was I really going to spend the rest of my life in that thing?

Some people don't really have a choice. Their legs just won't hold them up anymore. I thought hard about this. I wasn't paralyzed. I was not numb. Why couldn't I walk? I didn't know, but some people seemed to feel that I never would. Others counseled patience. I'm not a patient person. I also knew that the longer I was in that wheelchair, the harder it would be to get up out of it.

No one seemed to be in a hurry to get me walking again.

No one but me, that is. There seemed to be some sort of consensus that if I were meant to walk, I would walk. Later on. This wasn't good enough for me. I wanted to walk *now*.

During this time, I got my introduction to neurologists. The one that worked on me, Dr. Tang, paid me a surprise visit when I got out of ICU. The nurses whispered that he is one of the best in the world, and they were all aflutter because he was coming to visit. I was sleeping, of course.

I awoke to see a young man in a white coat standing at the foot of my bed, arms folded across his chest. He was very thin. He didn't say a word, just nodded at me and looked satisfied. I was alive, wasn't I? He had done his job, and done it well.

The next moment he was gone. That was the only time I ever saw him, this lovely stranger who opened up my skull and did something magical so I might live a few decades longer. He was careful to shave only the back of my head, mindful that I might want my long hair in the front for a while longer. So sweet! I ended up cutting my hair short, because having a buzz cut in the back and long hair in front just didn't do it for me. I love my new short hairstyle.

I ignored the fact that my short hair is out of necessity. It looks fashionable and is easy to take care of. At that point, that's all I cared about.

NEUROLOGISTS,
PART I

I ended up having three neurologists. The first one, that my brothers took me to see, was a dour older man who probably saw a lot, but who depressed me no end.

The waiting room was small and crammed with people. One of my brothers pushed my wheelchair in, and we sat in silence until my name was called.

When I finally got to see him, the doctor sized me up and put me through several "tests," one of which was walking to the end of the corridor and back. Of course I had a great deal of trouble doing it, as I was still impossibly dizzy and could only take a few wildly staggering steps until I retreated to the comfort of my wheelchair.

"You'll never walk again," he pronounced. "Some other things may or may not come back," he went on. "That remains to be seen."

My brothers drove me back to the rehab hospital in silence. We were all shocked and brought down by this assessment. I didn't accept it. *What does he know*, I thought. I wondered how he surmised I would never walk again when everything else was up in the air. I didn't say anything, but besides making me depressed, it made me angry.

I never went to see that guy again. The second neurologist was more upbeat but didn't seem to know much. I hit the jackpot with the third. She was knowledgeable, upbeat and very honest with me.

"It's amazing what people can do," Serena said. "You just never know what the future may hold, so I won't make any pronouncements."

By this time, I was walking (take *that*, all you naysayers). She gave me beta-blockers, which got rid of my tremor and made me feel generally terrific, but one terrible side effect was dizziness. Since I was dizzy to begin with, this was not okay, so I reluctantly had to give them up. Those beautiful beta-blockers. One of these days, I will try them again.

But I did walk from one side of her office to another under her watchful eye. I did not use any assistive device. No wheelchair, no walker, no cane. Mind you, the office was small and I crossed it in just a few steps. But still, I walked!

This neurologist was thrilled with my progress and encouraged me to do more, as if I needed encouragement. They should all be like this. Your mental condition is just as important as your physical one.

I left that office feeling on top of the world, and I'd tell anyone that if your neurologist doesn't make you feel that way, get another one. It's hard enough making a recovery. You don't need to be brought down, too.

EXERCISES FOR STROKE PEOPLE

I get asked repeatedly, *what exercises should I do?* That all depends on where you had your stroke and how severe it was. But these are the things that helped—and are still helping—me to get better.

The number one thing I hear about, and the number one problem I have, is with balance. I'm dizzy, dizzy, dizzy. The room is always spinning. I also have something called *ataxia*, fancy language for the two sides of your body feeling different. I have a lot to overcome!

Now, I've always been somewhat crooked. My mom used to complain when she did my hems. "Stand up straight. You're not standing straight."

Mom, I was. I was standing as straight as I could. I can't help it if I was born with a little ataxia.

I've always had balance problems. I couldn't, in the past, stand with my feet together, and putting one foot in front of the other, like models do on the runway, was impossible for me. But when I had a stroke, I no longer had any balance at all. It was wiped out. I would feel dizzy even when I was sitting still! Can you imagine falling from a sitting position? I could. I did.

My physical therapists taught me a few tricks to deal with my balance issues.

1. *Stand on one leg.* You have to hold on to something,

or you'll go right over. The kitchen counter worked for me. Or use a bedpost. Something you can't move, because this is hard. Having carpet on the floor helps. First do it with the left leg, then the right. Repeat until you get tired. Do this as often as you can, at least several times a day.

2. *Move your arms over your head.* You have to lie down first, on your back. Swing your arms up and over your head and lower them until your hands touch the floor behind your head. If you have ataxia, one arm may fly through the air and land first. This happened to me. I can tell how much progress I've made by the way my arms move.

3. *Stand and do some ballet.* If you don't know the positions in ballet, look at a book. I couldn't do this at first, although I was holding on to a bookcase. Now I can. Start in first position. Move your leg and point your toe in front of you, to the side, in back. Do the other leg. Do all five positions on each leg. This is not fun, especially at the beginning, but oh, does it teach you balance.

   As before, hold on to something that doesn't move. I wasn't able to do this very well at first. As my ataxia improved, I did it better and better. Then maybe let go of what you're holding onto. Maybe. I still can't do this, and it's been eight years. But…I can whip through those exercises as long as I hold on to the kitchen counter.

4. *Sit on the floor and raise your legs up.* Put your arms out, too, so you're balancing completely on your posterior. Sometimes I can do this, sometimes I can't. It strengthens your abdomen and greatly improves your balance.

5. *Walk, walk, walk.* I can't stress enough how important walking is. Use a walker if necessary, or a cane. You know what I hear most? With admiration? "Well, at least you're out there walking. Every day. Good for you!"

It may sound silly, but if you're female and of a certain age, when you were younger you might have walked around the house with books on your head to achieve good posture. As it turns out, it's also a great way to learn to walk correctly. So is balancing a cup of very warm tea (or coffee, or chocolate) in your hand while you walk, wobbling, from the kitchen to the living room. Talk about motivation! You do not want to spill that liquid, because not only can you hurt your feet, but if there are any spills, you'll have to go back and clean them up.

I found that I slowed down quite a bit out of necessity. I found that, if I didn't concentrate and my mind wandered, I would definitely spill. Ouch!

You would not believe how many times, in how many places, I put that cup down on the way to the living room. There are oases (read: tables) everywhere. Now I rarely spill. And I walk better.

When I was much younger, like in my 20s, I took ballet classes. Now, I was pretty bad at ballet, but I enjoyed doing it. I figured I was getting good exercise, and at the least, my posture would be great.

There was a young woman there who couldn't do anything. I figured no one could possibly be worse than me, but she was. No balance. She fell out of every pose. I thought at some point early on she would drop out of the class from embarrassment. She didn't.

After I was absent for about two months, I took another class at the next level. To my amazement, there she was! And guess what—she could do everything! Beautifully! I have not forgotten that girl, nor have I forgotten what she did. She must have practiced for hours each day, because believe me, she didn't have any innate abilities. I hope her whole life went like that. Slowly chipping away, ultimately successful.

Which leads me to the next point.

Do what you love. My physical therapist said this to me, and although I nodded, I really didn't understand what he meant. Do what you love! Especially when you can't do it.

Hiking. Bicycling. Tennis. Baseball. Ballet. Cooking. I could go on and on, but it really doesn't matter. Chances are, a stroke patient won't be able to do it, or will do it badly. No matter. Keep at it. It might take years, but one day you'll be able to do it again.

Case in point: I love to cook and bake. Now, when one hand shakes, or is paralyzed, or useless, you can't do this well. Let's not talk about all the burns I got, or how many things I spilled getting them out of the oven. Or how many times I asked other people to do it for me, because I knew I would drop it.

Well, you should see me now. I put things in the oven and take them out confidently and well. I've learned to crack eggs with one hand, my left (I'm a rightie). I still have some trouble measuring out vanilla, which takes two good hands, but I can get approximately a teaspoon. I use the mixer bowl to steady my right hand. There's almost always a solution.

The thing is, I never gave up. The thought of never baking a cake again was more than I could bear. What can you not bear the thought of never doing again?

Do it.

I Needed
Mental
Exercises, Too

There are few things more terrible than hearing someone say, "I can't do it," and watching them walk or wheel away. That's how you learn . . . nothing.

I've heard all the bromides about "If you believe you can do it, you can do it." This doesn't apply to everything. I've had dreams where I can fly, and I don't think I'm going to grow wings anytime soon. But also, in all my dreams I'm perfectly normal (well, as normal as I ever was), and I know I can achieve that. It's just a matter of believing it.

I've seen many people smile politely when I wax ecstatic because I can now climb to the third step on a ladder or bake lasagna. But I know better. I know that just a couple of years ago, I couldn't use a ladder at all. Then, my heart in my mouth, I climbed the first step. A few months later, I could do two steps. Now I can do three.

You'll get better no matter what. But to make real progress, you have to fiercely believe you can do it. The brain can make new connections and relearn to do a lot of things. You just have to be patient. Start small and repeat, repeat, repeat.

We have been so trained to expect immediate results. So if you're not better in a week, you give up. Yet it may take several months to see results, maybe a year or two. But if you give up trying because you don't have that mental stamina, you'll only make a little progress over the years.

Maybe no progress at all.

All appearances to the contrary, I firmly believe I am going to ride a bicycle again. I'm going to say "watch me," and triumphantly ride off (maybe into the sunset). Right now, I'm still afraid of falling on concrete (ugh!), and it's summer and way too hot to protect myself with lots of clothing. But one day I will do it. Just you wait and see.

LEARNING
TO WALK
AGAIN

I don't know how it happened. Someone somewhere along the line decided I could walk. Maybe it was the way I transitioned from the wheelchair to the bed—stood right up and swiveled around without complaint. Maybe it was something else.

One day, after breakfast and my morning nap (like an old, old person—or a cat—I took several naps each day), I was wheeled to a sort of gym. There I met Bret, my physical therapist, who would become so dear to me, but who (at that time) I thought of as The Evil One.

He was full of energy, bouncing on his toes in his tennis shoes as if he was about to burst out of his skin. So when introductions were made, and he said, "Ready?" I acquiesced, not knowing what I was in for.

It was not until Bret turned around that I saw them and froze—*the parallel bars*. Ever since high school gym, I had hated the parallel bars. I thought I was done with them for life. Yet there they were. Waiting for me.

Bret was waiting, too. "Now," he began, "we're going to take this nice and slow. Just do what you can."

Never had my wheelchair looked so good as then, when I had to leave it. There were two men assisting Bret. Assisting me, really. Bret bounded over the bars and hopped onto the extremely narrow walkway between them, positioned himself a couple of feet ahead of me, looked at me as I shook with fear, then coaxed, "Come on. I know you can do this."

Gripping the bars on either side of me, I slid one foot forward about an inch. And promptly started to fall. One of the assistants righted me as I gripped the bars harder. Slowly, I slid the other foot forward an inch, only my feet didn't line up correctly.

I was sweating. I hurt all over. My feet, my legs did not want to go. I felt as if I weighed five hundred pounds.

Bret didn't move. "All the way to me," he said.

Those were the longest two feet I have yet to encounter. Gripping those bars for dear life, I took a few more agonizing steps, then said in a small, garbled voice, "I can't do any more." Bret beamed. "You took eight steps!" he crowed.

The assistants put me back in my wheelchair. It felt heavenly. As a veteran of the New York City subways at rush hour, I knew how good a seat could feel. This felt better.

Bret came up to me before I was wheeled back to my room. "You see? You walked!"

"I wouldn't call that walking," I said.

"No? What would you call it then?"

I thought about that for a little while. Finally, "I don't know," I whispered.

Bret looked at me as if I were a doofus. "You walked. Trust me. You walked."

I GOT
MOTIVATED

Those struggling sessions with Bret continued. One day, my attendant left me at the rehab gym (in my wheelchair) about ten minutes early. Bret was working with another patient, so I just waited. It wasn't as if I had somewhere else to be.

It took me a few minutes to realize the guy he was working with had no legs. He was learning to walk with prostheses. I watched, fascinated, as he slowly and (I imagined) painfully took a few steps along those same parallel bars that were part of my torture routine.

I had nothing but admiration for that guy, and I wished him well. But that day I looked down at my lap and thought, *I am so lucky. I have legs.*

From that moment on, walking became an easier challenge. Whenever I thought I couldn't do it, I thought about that guy. And I tried harder.

There is always someone else worse off than you. Unless you are pushing up daisies, this is so true. I had all my limbs intact and my determination, which is boundless. I would learn the rest.

Is this easy? No. Is it fun? No. Is it possible? That would be yes. Almost anything is possible. All those "miracles" that people speak of have more to do with sweat than with what comes naturally. Walking did not, and still doesn't, come naturally to me. *But I can do it.*

I don't know how that guy lost his legs. At first, I thought he must have been a soldier, but I think Bret said something about his having been a basketball player. Maybe he was both. It sort of doesn't matter. He had grit and guts, which is all you really need.

HOSPITAL
ROOMMATES

I n real life, you usually get to choose your roommate. You can ask all sorts of questions—about their employment, what hours they keep, their habits, their friends—and hope that they aren't lying just to get a desirable place to live. Or, in some cases, *any* place to live.

Life's a game of chance, so maybe you say "Yes" to someone and hope for the best. Sometimes, you actually get it. Isn't that amazing?

At the rehab hospital, my roommate was an elderly, frail woman who was holding on for dear life to her last shreds of dignity. She did not know this; or perhaps she did; she only knew that she didn't want to move in with her daughter and son-in-law. Who could blame her? If I had a son-in-law like hers, I wouldn't want to move in with him, either. In fact, I would probably do him harm within twenty-four hours. Because he never shut up, and he was full of himself.

Every night, the daughter and son-in-law would arrive, and I would have to grit my teeth and get through the next two hours somehow. Every night, the ubiquitous privacy curtain got drawn. Too bad it didn't keep out voices! A semi-private hospital room, which is the only kind many health insurances will cover, is a great place to hear gossip, if that is your bent. If not, you're out of luck. You'll hear it anyway.

The elderly woman with the hard-to-take kids was debating whether she should move in with them? I voted *no*. Should she move into a nursing home? I voted *no* to that, too. Then there was a place 22 miles away where she'd have her own house and a modicum of independence. I voted *yes* for that one. But it was 22 miles away, and it would be inconvenient for the kids to visit her.

She feebly stood up for herself, saying the independent place would be good for her. The kids wanted her much closer to home. Round and round they went. Every night. Talk, talk, talk. And I had to listen to it.

She had had a stroke like me. It was not as bad, no permanent damage, but she was much older than I was and so it was harder to recover. This was a real dilemma.

She was a nice woman, but those kids...I wanted to put a muzzle on them. My own family and friends came to visit in the afternoons, never the evening. Maybe her family didn't have a choice. Maybe she liked them. Maybe I should just shut up.

This is what I mean. You've had a debilitating stroke, you're not in the best of moods. Your future looks murky. Now is not the time to have to put up with someone else's obnoxious children. In a hospital, you can't choose your roommates, that's for sure.

TEMPORARY
DOUBLE
VISION

I don't know how I developed it or when, but when I got to the rehab hospital, I had double vision. The clock in front of me, on the wall, told time twice—four o'clock, four o'clock. Everything appeared twice—my glasses, the chocolate bars on my tray, the cup of water the nurses had to hold for me because I was shaking so much.

Vision problems are common in people who have had strokes. Some people have double vision. Some people have tunnel vision. There may be partial blindness or total blindness.

Since the brain is right next to the optic nerve, and connected to it, this stands to reason. But the randomness of it takes your breath away. Sometimes there is just a millimeter between having no vision problems and being totally blind. The nurses seem to know when your vision problems are minor and temporary, as mine were. They never made a big deal out of it.

You might think it would freak me out to see the time twice, but it didn't. I had bigger fish to fry, such as learning to walk. And the nurses told me it would go away in a couple of weeks, and for once I believed them.

One day, I looked at the clock, and just like that, it showed the time only once. It had been about two weeks. The double vision was gone, never to return. Will the nurses be right about other things? That was so easy! If everything were this easy, having a stroke wouldn't be anything.

Unfortunately, it's not. Somehow, I got that little gift, but nothing else has been easy. And having a stroke *is* a big deal. Bigger than I even knew at the time.

HAVING
STRUCTURE
IN YOUR
LIFE

I may sound like a Montessori schoolteacher here, but it helps to get over a stroke when you have structure in your life. Get up at the same time each morning. Go to sleep at the same time each night. Take a part-time job, or volunteer somewhere. That way, you know what to expect, and can prepare for it.

If it's Thursday, it means you're going to work for four hours and then going to the gym. If it's Monday, you're reading and then cleaning the house, changing the sheets and towels. From a wheelchair, if you must. "The more you do, the more you can do." That's a direct quote from my brother Martin. He had a stroke, due to an auto accident, at 17. I would call him after my stroke many times, asking for advice. No one is as helpful as other people who have had strokes. Even if it's been decades, they still remember what helped them.

The hard part is doing something different at least once a week. Playing tennis. Going to Pottery Barn. Seeing a movie. Taking out the garbage. The point of this approach is to get your body to do things it doesn't ordinarily have to do. Like hitting a ball, dealing with stairs and escalators, or walking a lot.

Recently I traveled for the first time. I did not call the airport and request assistance, although I could have. I went through security, walked to the gate, got on the plane myself. I dealt with moving sidewalks and connections. I made it a little easier for myself by paying extra for seat assignments, because I know I can't scramble. I boarded early and asked the cabin attendants for help with the overhead bin, which is a joke for me, but people are very willing to do it for you.

So I proved to myself that I could travel by plane. Yay! I'll do it again, and it will be easier next time.

Recently, I met a man who had five—count them, five—strokes. The last one was the most damaging. He was paralyzed on one side. He came back in a year by playing tennis every day for hours (structure!). That was what he had always loved to do.

I had an occupational therapist who said to me, "It's very hard to believe in something that hasn't happened, and may not happen for a long time. You have to have faith."

My brother Martin said to me, "You'll only realize how much progress you've made by looking backward."

Both are so right. I believe in the body's power to heal itself. And I often find myself thinking, *I didn't used to be able to do that*. I didn't used to be able to step up on high curbs, walk on uneven ground, talk on the telephone. Now I can. So I guess I'm making progress.

Last night I sang a song from beginning to end. It's a silly song, but I could sing it recognizably. Not the way I used to, with a strong voice, but a couple of months ago I could only croak out a line or so. Because I'm so bored with reading out loud, I've decided to sing instead. Maybe boredom isn't a problem for you. You'd probably recover faster. But boredom is a problem for me, and although everyone needs structure in their lives, too much structure is, I find, a little boring.

PART TWO

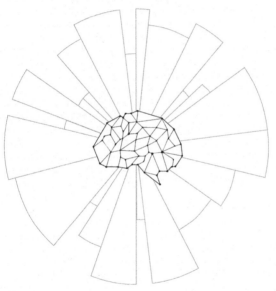

What
Would
Jill do?

I went to hear Jill Bolte Taylor speak, at a lecture series. The tickets were free. Some lovely neighbor had a subscription and had no interest in her, so she gave the tickets away. People would kill for tickets to this series, and they are quite expensive. I laughed all the way to the lecture.

Jill Bolte Taylor is a neuroanatomist, whatever that is, who had a stroke much worse than mine. You should see the picture she had the courage to publish. Maybe Frankenstein looked that bad, too. Even he didn't shave half his head of long, shiny blonde hair.

Taylor seemed perfectly normal at the lecture. So much so that I found myself gaping, and completely fascinated. She credits her complete recovery—which took many years—with the fact that people "left me alone."

When you've had a stroke, or any debilitating event or illness, you need a hero. Someone who is a shining example of what you can achieve. Never mind that you haven't achieved it yet. Jill makes me screw up my courage to ask "What would Jill do?" when I can't do something. The answer invariably has to do with patience, which I don't have enough of, and neither, I'm guessing, do you. It takes the patience of a saint when nothing happens for months at a time. Or years, maybe.

Speaking of patience, think of the way you were when

you were a child, when you had all the patience in the world. You had faith that someday you would be that elusive thing, a grown-up. In the meantime, you honed your skills by throwing a baseball, climbing up the jungle gym, riding your bicycle. Your brain was making those grooves, those connections. Which none of us, even Taylor, knew about. But they do now!

There's something called "muscle memory." If you do an action often enough, your body remembers how to do it. Seems we all were programmed to get over a stroke.

So there I was, worshipping Taylor, but that wasn't really enough. I got a dog, too.

Now, I love dogs. I'm what you would call a dog person. It's hard enough for me to walk down the street, but I do it with a dog.

No doubt tongues wag (they wag anyway). What am I doing with a dog when it's all I can do to take care of myself? Good question. Yet my dog forces me to bend and stretch, feeding her, brushing her, snapping on her leash, picking up after her.

I have to hold my own against a small but fierce 22-pound weight pulling against me and have excellent reflexes because, well, you never know what a dog will do. I have to feed her twice a day. And last but certainly not least, especially if you ask her, I have to play with her every afternoon. Throwing that squeaky toy until my arm is ready to fall off.

She makes me walk straighter. I have to watch out for squirrels and cats, because I'm in a lot of trouble if she sees them first. I not only have to control myself, but I have to control her, too.

I keep thinking about Jill Bolte Taylor. Does she have a dog? Would she approve of one? Maybe it's wishful thinking, but I feel she would.

A young child is the ultimate challenge; otherwise, get a dog. A dog forces you to move fast. Depending on the dog's age, you're up every few minutes. You have to yell at the top of your lungs a lot. You will use words you didn't know you knew. You will cuddle and coo.

You'll learn faster. You'll concentrate on something other than yourself. And, the dog doesn't care if you look or sound strange. Change is not threatening, either.

It's a win-win situation. Life should give us more of those.

When
Depression
Strikes

D on't you want antidepressants?" the hospital nurses
kept asking me. "Aren't you depressed?"
I didn't know what they meant. I had never tak-
en antidepressants. I knew what they were, of course. I had
been depressed, thought about taking them. But when I was
ready to call my doctor and make an appointment, my de-
pression was miraculously gone.

So I was not prepared for what hit me when I got home
from the hospital.

In the beginning, I was too confused to need antidepressants. I was busy learning to do laundry and wash dishes,
things I learned when I was 5, 6, 7 years old. Why learn
them again? In my case, it was because I had to learn to
do them with one hand. *That's* pretty depressing, but still I
resisted the call for help.

If I'm going to be depressed, I thought, *there had better
be a good reason for it.* You know what? There is.

At around month six, and don't ask me why I waited so
long, I realized that I had thoughts of killing myself almost
every day. Someone knows this, because first the nurses,
then the caregivers, don't let you have enough pills to do the
job. The caregivers watch you like hawks, doling out the pills
one by one, making sure you don't find the stash, wherever
they keep it. If you ask them, they put on an innocent face.

Who? Where? What? Suddenly they might claim, "My English is not so good." That's funny, it sounded really good only a moment ago. These women, so patient and giving in the face of a hard task, suddenly become silent when you ask them where the bottle of pills is. They know, and they disapprove.

So I asked for antidepressants. You never saw people move so fast in your life. I had that little pill in my hand that afternoon. I told myself that if I couldn't "touch" the unhappiness, couldn't feel it or get too close to it, I would be okay. And although they took about three weeks to work, the pills put up the barrier I was hoping for.

Time does work its magic. Now I can't remember how bad I felt. But it took me quite a while to get there.

A word to the wise: I don't care how proud you are, and no one can be prouder than me, take the antidepressants. If you had a stroke, you need them.

Now, when I get out of bed in the morning (notice I didn't say bound, I'm not there yet), it's hard to imagine feeling the way I did at my lowest. Even when you're surrounded by people who love you, you can feel bad. No one is to blame, and no one can make you feel better, but that little white pill can. All you have to do is swallow it once a day.

It must be so hard for men to do this, because they tend to avoid admitting defeat of any kind. But trust me, it's worth it.

Neurologists,
Part II

You can't shop around for a neurologist when you're unconscious. All you can do is live near a good hospital, hope your case is rare enough to challenge the surgeon in charge, and hope for the best. Without doing anything consciously, I managed to score on all three. But you know, it could have gone another way.

Thank you to Dr. Tang, wherever you are, for saving my life. Whatever you did. I met Dr. Tang once, in the hospital, when he stood at the foot of my bed with arms crossed in front of his chest and nodded at me. Mine was a challenging case, apparently. He rose to the occasion. Then he disappeared to that place where neurosurgeons go.

You tend not to think about things like this. I'm fond of saying, "Oh, who knows what the back of my head looks like under all that hair. Probably it's a mess of scars."

But Dr. Tang knows. He drilled a hole in my skull to relieve pressure. Possibly he vacuumed out the blood, too. Blood is a killer of brain tissue. I know this because I looked it up on the internet.

I relive that moment and think, was lying down a good thing? Blood pooled in my brain and wiped out my cerebellum, and a few other things. Yet if I'd remained sitting up, I might be paralyzed, at least partially. Because the blood would have run down my spine. Spinal cord injuries do not heal.

You can second-guess until the cows come home; it won't make a difference. You were going to be injured no matter what. A good neurological surgeon minimizes that injury. Maybe even makes it possible to reverse it eventually.

Dr. Tang said there was no reason why I eventually couldn't be normal. I still cling to that hope. But when brain tissue has died, it's dead. The way you can come back is to build new neural pathways beside the old, dead ones. This *can be done*, but it's not easy. Children recover faster because they are still learning. We adults, especially the older ones, have worn a very deep groove of learning and repetition. It's way harder to learn things all over again.

I once read a study of an experiment that was done in Japan. Toddlers and children under the age of 4 had half their brains removed, because of tumors or disease. After a year, they showed no difference from the children with their brains intact. *No difference. Half their brains gone.* It just goes to show how little of the brain we really need. In the future, when the brain is more understood, I believe machines (likely computers) will supply new neural paths quickly and efficiently. If your stroke doesn't kill you, you can recover fast.

I think Dr. Tang did a great job. And working on someone's brain requires a courage and skill that is very, very rare. But I don't think neurosurgeons realize that what they see vs. what you experience can be very different things.

It is *so hard* for an adult to learn to do something simple—like eat with a knife and fork—all over again. You rebel. You think, *I learned this when I was 3. And it was easy then!* It wasn't easy, and it took years until you could do it right. But you had a lot of patience then. And inspiration, because all the adults at the table used a knife and fork so elegantly. There were even stylistic differences. I'm thinking of the way Tony Soprano (James Gandolfini) ate his spaghetti. Even before the stroke, I couldn't do that!

I've long thought that actors have the easiest time relearning to do things, because they mimic other people all the time. Maybe I'm wrong, but actors have the patience to memorize scripts and learn to be someone else. In fact, they enjoy it.

I don't have what it takes to be a neurosurgeon, nor am I an actor. That puts me in the category of most people. Somehow, we need to be a little bit of the first, more of the second.

SHOE
FRENZY

My current neurologist is very cute, which draws my admiration (cute *and* a brain surgeon, that's quite a combination), but what captures my attention the most is that she wears fabulous shoes. She's stuck with that white coat, but she more than makes up for it with what's below her ankles. One time, she wore old-fashioned tap shoes, the kind that Ruby Keeler would wear. Another time, Grecian sandals, complete with long ties braided up her calves. I'm filled with longing about a lot of things, but those sandals most of all.

Now, most red-blooded American women love shoes. If you're a woman and you don't, what is wrong with you? You're a traitor to your sex. Go into the other room while I talk about this.

I have a shoe holder in my closet filled with beautiful shoes I cannot wear. Including a lovely pair of handmade black velvet shoes with slender, curving heels and a tight, narrow ankle strap that fastens with one tiny mother-of-pearl button. Don't even ask me about those heels, and especially not about those buttons. Everyone needs a goal, and those shoes are one of mine.

The day I can put them on, no sweat, and walk around without worrying that I'll fall over will be a banner day indeed. I hope I can applaud, too, because I think clapping will be in order.

I am counting the minutes until that happens. I want to walk in heels again. Stacked heels, kitten heels, stilettos, platforms, chunky, slender, it doesn't matter. Ankle straps! Mules! No-side shoes!

No *support* is more like it. It takes balance and strong foot muscles to wear these things. I'm stuck wearing sneakers and sensible flats, while I drool over the shoes in the Anthropologie catalog. So cute! So not for me!

Some people have an education savings account; I have a shoe account for the day when I can actually wear something fashionable on my feet. I just hope I'm not too old by then.

I have this fantasy—I walk into my neurologist's office wearing impossibly beautiful shoes, with impossibly high heels. She is amazed at the progress I've made. She doesn't even ask me to walk across her office, not after seeing me in those heels. We spend much of the time talking about shoes. We debate whose are prettier—hers or mine.

I fervently hope it comes true.

Reaching
The
So What Phase

I reached a point where what I call the *so what* factor took over. So it's been years and I still walk with a stagger. I don't talk very well. I'm still iffy on my right side.

So what?

For me, it's the little things that count. For instance, I can now reach up and hang a pot on my pot rack. I can climb up a small ladder. Crawl under the bed to retrieve something. I'm so proud of these things, but so *what?*

These are everyday things that most people don't think about. Except it may be a milestone for you to move your left forefinger. Be proud. Be exultant. But don't expect others to join in.

This is where you separate the men from the boys, so to speak. You live in the world of the disabled, and most people do not. They live in another world and have many problems to face. Only another stroke survivor knows what it means to move your finger, or put a pot on the pot rack.

This makes everything easier in a way. Bet you never thought about that! If you're concentrating hard on using the arm that doesn't work, you're not annoyed about the price of a gallon of gasoline. If you can barely walk or talk, you're not thinking about what to make for dinner. In other words, ordinary life, mundane annoyances, don't affect you. You have bigger things to think about.

Monks and others who hide themselves from the world on purpose train for years to achieve what you've achieved by having a stroke. *You* know what's important. It's a lesson you'll never quite unlearn. Many times I've heard people fretting about this or that and I wonder, what's all the fuss about?

Stroke survivors do not sweat the small stuff. That's why people often shrug and don't think it's a big deal that you're walking more smoothly. So what? It is a big deal to you. Much bigger than not getting into a movie because the line was too long and you were too late.

I keep making progress, and thank my lucky stars that I'm around to do so. But at a certain point, people won't react anymore. They still care, make no mistake about that, but they have moved on, and so must I.

THE LITTLE
BLACK
GLOVE

I gave in and ordered a fingerless glove that has a ½-lb. weight sewn in. It's like wearing a beanbag on your hand all the time. But against all odds, it's helping.

As I suspected, it didn't stop the shaking, but it slowed it down to where I can do certain things I couldn't do before. Like hold on to my granite counter in the kitchen. Zip up my jeans. It's still a bit of a struggle, but with the glove on I can actually button a button.

It's also giving my hand a workout all the time. When I take it off at night, my hand feels strangely light. But my fingers hurt, which I take as a good sign.

I didn't order the glove earlier because I knew it wouldn't help much, if at all. When I was in therapy, they tried all kinds of weights and none of them stopped the shaking. But now it's slowed way down and I felt I was ready for the glove. And it works a little.

Speaking of which—those exercises they make you do in therapy? I've been doing my own little survey. Sometimes I do them and sometimes I don't. Guess what? They work.

For example, I'd been drawing little circles and writing my initials with my right hand, wearing the glove and holding my thumb and forefinger with the left hand, because they're still so shaky. This sounds complicated, but it isn't.

By the twelfth day or so, I had gotten a little better at

drawing circles. But it was boring, so I stopped. Guess what? After a few days, I can hardly do it at all. I have to start from the beginning, although I expect it to go faster this time.

What if I'd done this every day for the last three years? Perhaps I could write just fine now. I've figured out that you need very intensive therapy, hours every day, to get better. It's too expensive to do. So until they can figure out a faster, easier, cheaper way, we're stuck with this imperfect approach. It's slow and cumbersome, and you make progress in tiny increments, but you do make progress.

I think this is the answer to the question of why some people seem to recover fully after only a year or so. It's because they get very intensive and targeted therapy for that year. The rest of us do not.

So you have to do it yourself. Every single day. It seems to be the only way for now. Maybe you have to continue therapy even after you get better, I don't know (but I'll tell you when the time comes).

ADAPTATION
VERSUS
LEARNING

How do you know if you're adapting or learning? In some cases, it's transparent. I type with one hand. That's adapting. If I tried to use my right hand (the one that's been affected by the stroke), it would take an hour to write a single email. I don't know who has the patience for that. Certainly I don't. So I've adapted.

On the other hand, every night I practice flipping cards or coins with my right hand. It's hard. The hand just doesn't want to cooperate. That's learning. Bret told me, "Only do things you're successful at. Otherwise, you'll be so frustrated that you'll give up." Good advice, but you'll never learn that way. Flipping cards, for instance. I'm not good at that. Yet, I think I'm just a little bit better after doing it for three weeks. That's enough to make me do it again and again. One day, I'll do it smoothly and comfortably.

To live your life, you have to adapt. But to get better at something, you have to learn. This is such a tall order that I hardly know where to begin to give you or any stroke survivor advice about this. Clearly, you have to do both.

But doing both is time-consuming and frustrating. Not to mention confusing. I can open a cabinet door with my bad hand, but the good one now reaches out automatically to do it. The good hand can do it faster, and I don't have to think about it. So which hand should I use?

The good hand has adapted nicely. The not-so-good one needs to learn. I compromise by often using two hands to open a cabinet door.

Everyone needs to come to their own conclusion about this. Just be aware of one thing: you'll never learn anything if you refuse to develop what doesn't work.

LIFE IS
NEVER
THE SAME

I had what I thought was a pretty good life. A good, fairly secure, well-paying job just 15 minutes from my home. In fact, when my former dog got old, frail, and sick, I came home at lunchtime every day to take her for a midday walk and love her up a little. It wasn't much, but it made a difference.

I had a lovely home, a 1928 house that I had extensively remodeled. My job allowed me to stay there. One paycheck covered the mortgage, the other paid bills and property tax. There wasn't much left over, but it was enough, and I was happy.

I had lots of friends, a rich social life. Oakland has a lot of great restaurants, so I was never lacking for good food. I lived near UC Berkeley, so there were lots of classes. I traveled when I could. Boyfriends came and boyfriends went, some of them staying for quite a while.

I thought I pretty much had a good life. I had it all planned out—work for another seven or eight years, then take it easy somewhere. A little rose-covered cottage by the sea where I could read, garden, and walk to my heart's content. Continue entertaining, which I always enjoyed.

The stroke changed everything. You are never the same. Even if you recover fully, you are never the same.

After a stroke, you know for certain that you are mortal.

Tragedy can strike at any time. Disability is just around the corner. For most people, frailty comes slowly, and there is a long, long march towards the end. When you have a stroke, you lose everything all at once.

I jokingly call it "instant old age," but it's no laughing matter. Suddenly, you can't do things you've been doing since childhood. Like tying your shoelaces. Making breakfast. Answering the door. Talking on the telephone. Eating soup (that spoon!).

It all eventually comes back, or you learn to compensate, but your life is turned topsy-turvy. There are certain things you may never do again. I'm still waiting for the time when I can ride a bicycle or hike a trail. Will I ever? Who knows?

For me, the sudden loss of my job was shocking. After I realized I would never go back (and that took over a year) I mourned it for a long time. My job made everything else possible. No one really discusses finances with you, but it's a cold, hard reality that sets in after you get over the initial shock. Health insurance is great, but there are a few things it doesn't cover, and you can be responsible for thousands of dollars in healthcare bills. Not to mention paying for the caretaking you're going to need.

I had been very stressed before the stroke (BS) more than I realized. I broke up with my live-in boyfriend of thirteen and a half years. My mom died. My dog died. I lost my business of seventeen years. One of my brothers went into renal failure and needed a kidney. I was a top candidate for something bad to happen.

"When sorrows come, they come not single spies but in battalions." Shakespeare, and it's so true. To make ends meet, I took a job at a bank, and within six months the Great Recession of 2008 came along. There was a silent run on the bank I worked for, and over the weekend, we got sold. Never again would I have fun at work.

On the stress scale of one to ten, I was about a fifteen. Everybody says, "Oh, I'm so *stressed*," but I really was *stressed*. And not the kind you can just work off at the gym.

No sooner did I get onto the road to recovery from one thing when *wham*! I was hit with something else.

I told myself, You must endure, keep calm and carry on and all that, but my body felt differently. First I got a skin disease, then I had a stroke. *Stop, stop!* The message was coming in loud and clear, but I didn't pay it any attention.

One of my yoga teachers used to say, "Boring is good." There is a high price to pay for a life of high adventure. I had the thrills, but I also ended up with the illnesses. Now I'm content with so much less, and I intend to continue this way. So should you.

BS, AS*

As I write this, I'm at five years, four months. My friends are impatient because I'm not fully recovered yet. But when I hear people say, "I had a stroke twelve years ago," or fifteen, or twenty, I understand. Even if you've fully recovered, your life is not the same.

A stroke is a pretty serious wake-up call. Everyone knows that eventually they will die, but until you have a brush with death, it's just an abstract notion. If you've had a stroke, you *know* you're going to die. Any minute now. But possibly not for thirty, forty, fifty years. It's wild, and it's sobering.

You learn quickly to focus. Along with putting one foot in front of the other, which comes so easily to most, you ask yourself, *what do I really want?* For some, it's a switch in careers. For others, it's the end of any notion of a career.

For myself, I suppose I could now return to some sort of work if I wanted to. But I find I don't. Work doesn't have meaning any more. I worked hard, and it just made me sick. So I take every day as it comes. Some days I want to do things, some days I don't. It's all right with me either way.

---

*Before Stroke, After Stroke

STROKES
AND
STABILITY

You thought I was going to talk about physical stability, right? Well no, I'm talking about mental stability.

I got this idea when a friend mentioned how comforting her home was. My home is comforting, too. But not completely.

After you've had a stroke, you don't feel stable anymore. Anytime. Anywhere. The world can come crashing down on you in a nanosecond, and your whole life can change in an instant. It already has.

Home is not necessarily the sanctuary it used to be for me. I had my stroke at home. I had a hard time going into my bedroom again, where it happened, but I forced myself to get back on the horse. You have to.

Or not. But if you don't, you're inviting another phobia in the door. I don't know about you, but I don't need another one of those. I have enough of them, thank you.

Although my neurologist (the one with the cute shoes) said I'd never have another stroke, I have my moments. When I get into bed, for example.

Most nights I'm so tired that it's a relief to crawl between the covers. All I have left to do is read a few pages and turn off the bedside lights. But there are those nights I think, *what if I have another stroke right now? Will I have the presence of mind to call 911? Who will take care of my dog?*

Once in a while, I work myself into a real frenzy. I think I'm having a stroke. Then I think, *what if I never have another stroke?* Then I'm getting all worked up for nothing.

Life and death are still mysteries. I'm getting philosophical, but that's my way of avoiding having to read out loud. I hate it, but it's helping me to get my voice back.

Rs are still hard to pronounce, and Ss make my front teeth literally grind. I get out of breath easily. All I can think of to do is practice, practice, practice. I may get to Carnegie Hall before I can speak properly.

I started this chapter talking about comfort, so I'll end it talking about comfort. Who out there has had a stroke and feels comfortable? Who doesn't have the sword of Damocles hanging over their head? Actually, I'd like to meet that lucky person, because it takes real talent to be able to forget like that. Maybe I'd learn a thing or two.

Listen, all of life is extremely uncertain. As stroke survivors, we just know it better than some, that's all.

Having a stroke changed me in other ways, too. Here are some of the things I did before I had the stroke:

1. Ran
2. Hopped
3. Skipped
4. Danced
5. Walked everywhere
6. Hiked mountains and forest paths
7. Rode a bicycle
8. Piloted Cessnas
9. Paraglided
10. Traveled
11. Practiced yoga for 20 years
12. Began t'ai chi

And I didn't consider myself a physical person!

Now...I can't do most of those things. I'm happy to seat myself in a movie theater. But I just watched a program on TV about a guy who had a paragliding accident, and spent four months in the ICU. The doctors said he would spend the rest of his life in a wheelchair. Now he is perfectly normal. Those are my heroes.

So I have to ask myself, did any of that physical stuff mean anything? We define ourselves by what we do, but what happens when you can do much less than you used to?

I don't think of myself as disabled, though I am certainly that. In fact, I'm shocked when I see myself in a mirror in a store, because I topple and weave so much. If I didn't have my cane, I think people would assume I was terribly drunk. Yet I'm always surprised. *Oh, I'm disabled. Fancy that.*

PART THREE

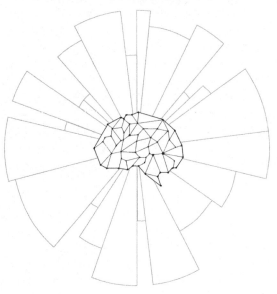

RETURNING TO
A MORE
NORMAL LIFE

Everyone has the same goal: to return to the life they led before. Suddenly that life looks great, whether it was or it wasn't.

What's the difference? Then, you had more choices. Now, you're limited. Think about that. *You had more choices.* Maybe you didn't use them much, but you had them. And they were great.

I love having options, and as I get more normal, I have more of them. They're mitigated by two things, though: COVID and falling. Because of COVID I can hop in the car and go…where? I don't want to be near crowds, indoors is scary, people are suspect. Airports are not safe places. No one really knows what the rules are, and they keep changing anyway.

COVID is bad enough, but for stroke survivors there's also the fear of falling.

In the beginning, I fell a lot. Like, several times a day. When I turned the TV off at night, for instance, and I had to stand up and walk across the room to turn the lights off, I always took a deep breath first. And wondered if I could do it.

I had no balance. That got wiped out in the stroke, and no matter how smart you are, how thoughtful, you can't stay upright if you don't know which way is up. I hear scientists and doctors are working on a remedy for this—but in the meantime, there's no other way but to learn it the hard way.

I used the walls a lot. And the furniture. Anyone looking

at me would think I was a blind person, and sometimes I thought I knew how it must feel to be blind.

I had a tendency to keep going when I needed to stop. If I were going left, I would fall to the left. If I were going right, I would fall to the right. Since I often get left and right confused, all I knew was I fell.

I told Bret "If you don't fall, it means you haven't tried, right?" He blanched—the first time I ever saw him do that. And was silent. Because it's true and it's not true.

I was lucky, oh, was I lucky. I only broke a leg, and that happened because my dog went berserk and ran in all directions at once, or so it seemed. I fell on my leg and broke it.

After that, I learned how to fall. You see those stunt people in movies rolling with the punches? I had to learn to do this. As I go down, I make sure I land on my butt. It's full of bruises, but at least it's fleshy and I don't break any bones. It works 90% of the time. The other 10%, I fall on my bony arms (ouch), or worse, hit my head hard just when I think I'm safe (double ouch). Once I even raised an egg on the top of my head, which scared me to pieces, but apparently it didn't do any lasting harm, because I'm still here.

I must have been quite a sight, Band-Aids everywhere, full of scabs and bruises. My friends would look, and thankfully not say anything, but I saw their eyes go wide. I knew they were afraid for me, but they also know how headstrong I am. I'll listen politely, then do what I want.

Please, don't do it my way. I wished I had someone to tell me this, but I didn't. If I had it to do all over again, and I sure hope I don't, I would learn to crawl first, like a baby, on all fours. This is HARD, but if you master it, you can start to get up. Like a toddler! They learn, don't they? They learn fast. They fall a lot, too. That doesn't stop them. They get up and try again, until they can do it. Then they feel very pleased with themselves as they teeter off into the sunset.

We can all learn from them. We were that way, too, once. To recover from a stroke successfully, we all need to learn to channel our inner babies.

Time, Interrupted

Time changes when you've had a stroke. Suddenly it takes ten minutes to tie your shoelaces, when it used to take ten seconds. WTF? You learn to leave extra time for doing everything.

Then there's what the therapists and nurses tell you.

"Eventually the shaking will stop. Eventually you'll be able to use that hand. Oh, eventually you'll be ambidextrous." Eventually. Eventually.

Just how long is eventually? I'm in my fifth year, and my hand still shakes. It has slowed down, but I still break and spill things. How long will this last?

I've tried, and failed, to write my name hundreds of times. I've given up, from futility and boredom. Yet, giving up brings its own set of problems. There's "learned nonuse" for example. In other words, use it or lose it. I think I'm losing it.

"Do what you love," therapists and nurses told me repeatedly. They clearly learned it from some book, but there's more than a grain of truth in it. So I find myself sort of dancing to my favorite tunes, even though my right leg won't cooperate. The rest of me does. I haven't yet gotten up the courage to buy a ball and bounce it (yikes!), although I'm sure that will help a lot. I can measure out a teaspoon of vanilla. Doesn't everybody love chocolate cake?

I met a guy at the movies, another stroke survivor. He was completely paralyzed on one side, but overcame it by hitting a tennis ball repeatedly. "At first, I couldn't do it at all," he said. "I missed the ball completely. But suddenly I could make contact with that ball and hit it. Then I could hit it over the net. Then I tackled backhand. I've never looked back." Now, he added, I'm as good as I ever was. "And I can do everything else!"

In just a year, he made a full recovery. And was cheerful about it. "Keep up the good work!" he counseled me. I looked at him, hale and hearty. Rushing into the cinema to get a good seat. You would never know. Will I ever reach that point?

THE
FATIGUE
FACTOR

You hear it from everyone who's had a stroke. "I'm tired." Sometimes it's more than that. "After I do anything, I want to take a nap. What's up with that?"

I'm antsy, so I'm less tired than that. But I can relate. For the first two years, sleep was like the Holy Grail. In fact, for year one, I did little else. My sofa can attest to that. Caregivers came and went. It was all a blur to me, because I just wanted to sleep. Me, who was always busy. I was tired all the time!

My friends who came to visit me at the hospital brought books, because they often had to sit there for a half hour or so until I woke up and saw them. Then I thought to myself, *better get up now. You have to carry on a conversation.*

And I did rally to the occasion. But there always came that moment when I wished they'd go home, because I wanted to nap again—and it had only been 45 minutes. I didn't want to be rude, but oh, how I wanted to sleep. I felt like Oliver Twist. "Please, sir, I want some more."

Bless my favorite caretaker, because she dragged me to shopping centers and made me stay up to watch TV with her. Even then, sometimes I succumbed and fell asleep.

You become the consummate bore. You can put anybody to sleep, because guess what? That's all you want to do, anyway.

Then one day you wake up and think, *I can't (yawn) spend the rest of my life sleeping. I just can't.*

That's when you begin, in earnest, building up your stamina. You have to do this a little bit at a time, because if you try to sink or swim, believe me, you'll sink. It took me two or three years, but one day, I realized *you're pretty normal.* I never nap anymore. I get out, drive around, go here and there, take classes, garden, fly long distances, etc. I know not to schedule more than three things in a day, but that's probably good to do even if you didn't have a stroke.

True, I have to be more careful. I go out less at night, because when I get tired, I can't walk very well, and I wouldn't give you two cents for my vocal abilities. (That's okay, my dog still loves me.)

I can drive late at night, but do I want to? That would be no.

So I don't beat myself up because I tire easily. It comes with the territory. Just work on doing a little bit more, then a little bit more than that. Soon you'll surprise yourself with what you can do. I'm not talking about walking tightropes and climbing mountains here. Just getting through a normal day can feel like you've been in a circus. In a good way.

FRIENDSHIPS

They say when you have a stroke you lose half your friends. Possibly this is true. You are not the same physical person, after all. Those who have come to rely on you for doing certain things—a gym friend, for instance, or a hiking buddy—may fall by the wayside because you simply can't do those things anymore.

I'm not mad. In their shoes (sneakers, probably) I might have done the same. And they are hurting, too. They want their best bud back! The one who could do anything! And have a glass of wine afterward.

Hopefully, someday, a stroke survivor may be able to do this. Your friends may have moved on by then. But they may be delighted that you can once again hike, or go to the gym, or whatever. It's better that they *not* know how much you struggled to get to that point.

Then there are the friends that you went to the movies with, had dinner with, played chess with. Discussed books with. More wine! You can still do all of those things, although the doctor may say you have to limit the wine. (I don't. Sometimes you just have to say, *screw it.*)

You may find, as I did, that the people you love the most, and who love you, will stick by you loyally as you recover. It helps if you recognize that this is not easy for them, either. The carefree, fun-loving person they knew has changed dramatically. Overnight.

Joke about what you can't do! "Uh, I don't think I can carry a case of beer. But if you have a teenager around . . . " (They get a bad rap, teenagers. There's nothing like having a young, strong, healthy person around when you need them most. And they love to help, so send me your teenagers if you don't want them!)

A lot will depend on what kind of stroke you had, how bad it was, how it left you. If you're housebound, it will be harder. People now have to make an effort to see you. Some of them just won't. You have to learn to shrug it off. You may find yourself shrugging more of the time than you want to.

Okay, if your life has changed, shouldn't your friendships change, too? New people await you. They didn't know you before, so your disability is part of who you are. I'm "the lady with the cane." I've come to cherish that moniker, although I'm already learning to walk unaided.

There are some horror stories, and I have one. A friend and neighbor, whom I'll refer to as Marcia (that is not her name), actually went up and down the street I lived on with a petition to stop me from driving. She did this behind my back, not a word to me. I only found out about it because the DMV contacted me.

The lady at the DMV was quite sympathetic, a trait you don't often associate with them. "There are tyrannical neighbors everywhere," she said, sighing. "You wouldn't believe the things I've seen." (Actually, yes, I would.) "Unfortunately," she went on, "because we're a public agency and have to take every complaint seriously, we're going to have to test you again."

I had to go through the whole rigmarole to get my license reissued. I got a permit immediately, but I had to take the written exam and a driving test. It took me a great deal of time, not to mention money. So my so-called friend and neighbor Marcia didn't gain a thing. Except maybe a sense of righteousness, as she was "protecting" everyone. But she wasn't protecting me. Ultimately, she didn't accomplish her goal, but she did lose a friend.

Many people will tell you over and over what you can't do. It's in their best interest to keep you safe. After all, if you don't do much, you can't hurt yourself. But if you're ever going to get better, you have to ignore them when you want to learn things, and think you eventually can. Just don't tell anyone about it.

Don't Listen
to Anyone

Jill Bolte Taylor, who should be called the Patron Saint of Strokes, says she got well *(all the way)*, because everyone left her alone. Which means you shouldn't listen to other people, no matter how well meaning they are. Only listen to your own body. It speaks volumes.

My favorite physical therapist told me the same thing. "Don't listen to anybody, including me," he said. That's a big responsibility, but I took it on. Because no one knows my body and my personality as I do.

Case in point: Like everyone else, I was born with two parents. (Unlike many others, they actually stayed together.) But Mom would get hysterical if you cut your finger. You lost so much blood (a few drops) that you must be dying. Make the funeral arrangements!

Dad, on the other hand, was cheerful and optimistic even if you *were* dying. They're both gone, but guess which one I'd rather have around now?

One thing is for sure: when you have a stroke, you find out who your friends really are. And a lot of them will take their cues from you. Do you act devastated, like your life is over? I wouldn't want to be around you, either. On the other hand, if you're always hopeful, always trying, your friends, like mine, will bend over backwards for you. They'll be like the one who, after twenty-five years, got her front cement step repaired because I told her it scared me. I probably wasn't the only one who complained about it, but I like to think she did it mostly for me.

Now I visit her more often. It's not scary to walk up those steps anymore!

THE CLOAK
OF INVISIBILITY

Superheroes unite! Being handicapped is the closest you'll ever come to being one of them. How in the world can you be a superhero when you can't walk a straight line? It's easy, actually.

One of the first things I noticed about being disabled is that when it comes to a lot of things, people sensitively leave you out of the conversation. Work, for instance. People talk about work all the time. Only now, if you're truly disabled and can't work, people won't mention it in front of you. The same is true about hiking, surfing, walking in the woods. Anything physical, actually. Which is how most people blow off steam when they're not working.

You're left sitting quietly, twiddling your thumbs (if you can), like people in days of old. Visits become front-parlor affairs. If you don't know the person, or the people, well, you rack your brains for something to talk about. Because they've been bounding around doing things, which, if you're a stroke survivor, you can't. You're not part of that world anymore.

But, if you choose, you can gleefully become invisible. Sit in places, like coffee shops, where people will ignore you. You'll be amazed at the things they say in front of you. Like their spouse is having an affair, and they know about it but don't want to rock the boat. *(That boat has already been rocked.)* Like how much money they have embezzled from their employer. (Some people take hundreds of thousands

80

of dollars, and feel justified in doing so. Yikes!) One woman at Starbucks said "If my husband died tomorrow, it would be fine with me. All I really care about is the children." *(Uh, they're his children, too.)*

Because if your legs don't work right, your brain doesn't either, right? So they can say anything! Liberating for them, yes, but it can be shocking to you.

This happened less and less as I got better, so I enjoyed it while I could. I'll never get another chance to be a superhero. With a cloak that made me invisible.

Six Years
and
Counting

On May 29, 2019, I had the sixth anniversary of my stroke. It was a strange day. I felt as if I should be celebrating, but what? Staying alive, maybe? Six years ago, I almost died but didn't. Does that sound better?

I could be sad and mourn the life I lost. To be honest, I don't remember much of it. I've been so busy learning new ways to do old things. Like walking, talking, and writing. (Do I focus on these things too much? They are so basic, and it's so frustrating when you can't do them.)

It used to be that I went for long stretches without changing much. Now I'm a different person every few months. Obviously, I'm still recovering.

If you had told me during year one that I would not be normal yet at six years, I would have been disbelieving. What, me? Yet here I am, still making progress and learning new things. It's humbling, and I don't mean that in the Academy Award way. No one is giving out any prizes for how far I've come.

A few months ago, in a fit of I don't know what, I signed up for two classes: Balance and Flexibility and Gentle Yoga.

Balance and Flexibility is a hoot. The teacher, Sue, is very funny (they should call it Balance, Flexibility, and a Comedienne). In the beginning, I couldn't even walk across the room, and I needed the ballet barre for everything. I fell two or three times, even though Sue said the first rule was "Don't fall!" Sorry, Sue, you didn't know you had a rebel on your hands.

We do silly things like walking and kicking up behind us (Sue calls it "The mule kick.") It feels ridiculous, but I guess it's working because I can walk across the room now, and I can do a lot of things without the barre.

Gentle Yoga was a revelation. I should start by telling you that in my former life, Before The Stroke, I was a real yogini. Twenty years of almost daily yoga will do that to you.

I knew I'd reached some sort of milestone when I realized how much I missed my yoga classes. So, after six years of not doing any yoga at all, I signed up for Gentle Yoga. Not a beginner's class, because I knew all the poses and then some, but nothing too strenuous.

In the beginning, I shook and fell a lot. I didn't think it was possible to fall when you were sitting on the floor to begin with, but I did. I lay there like a fish flopping in an inch of water. And I thought my balance had gotten pretty good!

There were poses I didn't even try, because I knew I couldn't do them. Simple lunges, for instance. I used to privately call my former teacher The Lunge Queen, but as much as I disliked them, I did them. Now I couldn't see how it was possible to bring your leg forward like that. Mine just refused to move.

This is a testament to getting better by doing what you love. Because of yoga class, I can now sit cross-legged on the floor, and yes, do lunges, with better balance. I'm not afraid to stand on two feet on a yoga mat without falling. Stand, mind you, not sit.

Then there is my teacher, Cassie, a pistol if I've ever seen one. She talks quite a bit, and it's possible to let her voice be background noise, but I listen to everything she says. I've had epiphanies because of her. For instance, she says (over and over again), "If you shake, it means you are trying too hard. Back off a little." Whoa! I shake a lot! So I've been practicing not trying so hard on the right side, and guess what? The shaking is slowing down, in some cases even stopping. I think I've found some sort of key.

The other day she had us "flossing" nerves. Now, I don't know about you, but I've only ever flossed my teeth. But it sounded good, so I flossed my nerves, too. Especially since it was so easy. You just gently run your hands up and down the meridians (don't ask; I depend on Cassie to tell me what to do.)

Nerves, I'm finding out, have memories as well as muscles. Flossing them wakes up those memories.

You learn something new every day.

Why am I telling you all this? I've never forgotten that guy at the cinema, who was paralyzed on his right side (after a stroke), and came all the way back by playing tennis, something he loved and was good at. In fact, he was a professional player, so he had even more incentive to get better. His livelihood depended on it.

Is there anything you have lost the ability to do? Whether it's something simple like walking, or something more complex like tennis, maybe you can do it again. It's going to take a lot of practice, and a lot of failure, but one day you might surprise yourself.

I see a lot of people in wheelchairs, fists clenched because they never learned to unclench them, or hands never raised because they're not under good control, being wheeled around by a relative because they can't afford a motorized wheelchair (very expensive); they are dependent, eyes shining with desire to be let out of their cage, yet completely resigned to their fate. Is this you? It certainly isn't me.

Maybe it's *not* your fate. Maybe you can walk, play tennis, dance, ride a bicycle. You have to not take "no" for an answer. I didn't. Not that I'm any great shakes (no pun intended), but I just won't quit.

THE
POWER
OF MUSIC

Now, this is a true story. I say this because if someone told it to me, I would be pretty skeptical. But I was there. I saw it with my own eyes.

I was in a therapy appointment, playing patty-cake with Marilyn—a child's clapping game, but I could do it well only with one hand.

Bret was in the therapy room, a sort of gym for misfits like me. He was training a young man, who was kind as could be but clearly bored and antsy. The guy, whose name I forget, brought a guitar with him, obviously his first love.

The young man picked up his guitar and started to play. Something complex, with a strong beat and a melody that made you want to run to the center of the dance floor and let loose. It was ironic, really, because the few people in the room were mostly in wheelchairs.

Everyone froze, myself included. Then, patients and therapists alike, people in wheelchairs, people who couldn't take three steps without falling over, started dancing. Standing up! Nobody fell!

The room was rockin' out. For a few minutes, no one was brain injured. Therapists forgot their roles. Everybody danced. Some, my therapist Marilyn included, were *great*.

Then the song ended, and everybody went back to what they were doing. But there was now a buzz in the air, a little excitement, a little electricity. What was going on?

Was music that powerful? Were people, even the brain-injured and stroke patients, capable of much more than everyone thought? Did that include me?

Fast forward six years or so. I'm browsing in Barnes & Noble when "Give Me That Old Time Rock and Roll" starts playing on the loudspeaker. In five seconds, I'm dancing along with the rest of the patrons on the first floor, and my balance is suddenly perfect.

When people get older, they tend to want the atmosphere quiet, but I wonder. Music is used for all kinds of things, from calming crying babies to helping surgeons concentrate in operating rooms. Maybe music also could make patients get better faster.

Learned
Non-Use

Just as we learn to use things, we learn to *not* use things. I wish I had a dollar for every time I've said, "You sit in that wheelchair for years, and you're going to get really good at sitting in a wheelchair. But your legs will forget how to walk."

People don't listen. I might as well talk to the sky. They nod and smile, agree with me, then wheel away. They've already made up their minds that they can't be helped, and that I am so wrong.

Do you know who Tiger Woods is? Most people do, because of the scandal and the car accident. Forget about those for a minute, because he's a great golfer. Mr. Cool won lots of trophies at prestigious golf clubs around the world. The Augusta at Georgia. Pebble Beach. *Those* kinds of clubs.

This wouldn't impress me, but I've played golf, and it's *hard*. Getting that little ball into that little hole in the grass can have you drenched in sweat when it isn't even that hot outside.

Tiger Woods had it all. He was at the top of his game, and although some champions had the guts, it was kind of a joke to play against him. He won almost all of the time.

Then he announced that he was changing his swing, learning a new one. *What?* He had won so many tournaments with his swing! What was wrong with it, anyway?

Lots of people would have *killed* for that swing.

But he knew it wasn't right. So he took a few years off to learn and practice a new swing.

Golf swings, walking, talking, all cut a deep groove in your brain that is nearly impossible to erase. Nearly.

When Tiger Woods finally made it back to the circuit, he had to start from zero. He didn't win tournaments. His swing looked a bit unnatural. Everyone thought he had made a big mistake. Maybe he thought so, too.

But then he started to win, and win big. He took home lots of gold trophies, and lots of money (philandering is expensive).

What is the moral of all this? That it's okay to change your golf swing? (I never had a swing to begin with.)

Of course not. Stroke survivors assume that they can't play golf. But there are two grave mistakes we can make. I say *we* because I've already made both of them.

The first mistake is learned non-use, as in "My right arm doesn't work, so I think I won't use it." You're wearing a deep groove that says, "Don't use that right arm! For anything!"

Maybe you shake. Maybe you're paralyzed. Maybe the arm doesn't know where it is in space. Don't use it! Keep it in your lap, frozen forever instead!

I am guilty as charged, and boy, am I sorry. My right arm only works for large motor skill things, which allows me to take out the trash but makes washing my hair a challenge. I am now trying to learn a new swing.

The second mistake is adaptation, such as "My right arm doesn't work, so I'll get very good with the left." (Throat clearing.) I'm writing this book with my left hand, so guilty again. This must be very common, because my OT's parting words to me were, "Don't get too good with that left hand!"

They are both understandable, but very hard to undo. You have to train all over again, and you are so tired of training. Better to do it right to begin with.

The longer you avoid doing something, the more the

status quo gets reinforced. This goes for anything, not just strokes. It's a Catch-22. You can't really do it, so you don't, so your body gets used to not doing it. Pretty soon it becomes part of your story. I'm still telling people I'm not good at math. The truth is, I am, I'm just better at things that require language skills. But I've done a good job of convincing people, including myself, that I'm not good at math. I can figure out the restaurant tip in a nanosecond. But I let somebody else do it.

In life, you can get away with this. I'm sorry to say, when you've had a stroke, you often can't. There's that moment when nobody is around and you have to climb that ladder. Some people just wait until someone is available. I'm too impatient for that. Normally, that's not such a good trait. But when it comes to getting over a stroke, it is.

Hɪp Hɪp
Hooray

Sometimes you hear something over and over, but it just doesn't register. It might as well be a wall of words. You just hear, "Blah, blah, blah, blah." Then one day you wake up and listen, and the effect can be electrifying.

For months, my yoga teacher, Cassie, has been saying, "All movement begins in the hips." My reaction was to tune her out. And then one day she said it, and it was like a revelation. *All movement begins in the hips.*

I got excited and went home and took my dog for a walk. This time, I paid attention to what my hips were doing. To my surprise, they were all over the place. They swung a lot when I walked. Sometimes, my hip kicked out before my leg did. Wrong!

I made a conscious effort to keep my hips still, and when I succeeded, I could walk almost normally. With a gliding motion, it was even easier.

What does this mean? *All movement begins in the hips.* When I do it right, my bad leg actually aches. It's a good ache!

Recently, in yoga class, we practiced foot stuff. I've always been a supinator, meaning I walk with my weight on the outside of my foot. Pronators walk with their weight on the inside. Most people fall into the supinator or the pronator category. It's rare to find a person who actually puts their weight equally on the inside and outside of their feet.

Big yawn. Who cares, right? Well, when balance becomes an issue, you should care. Because you're never going to learn to walk again *without limping* unless you put your weight in the right place.

This is easier said than done. When you're recovering from a stroke, and you have to learn basic things all over again, you have to learn them correctly or it doesn't work. When you learned these things the first time, as a toddler, you also learned to compensate. If you put more weight on the outsides of your feet, for instance, you learned to walk a little differently to make up for it. (That's one reason people have different gaits.)

When you're learning it *again*, the compensation business doesn't work. You have to learn it correctly or else. So now you don't just have to learn to walk, you have to learn all of the elements of walking and do every one of them well. Having a stroke makes you very smart.

Some people are so horrified by this that they just don't learn at all. Believe me, I understand. But I'm just not built that way. Tell me I can't do something—and watch me try, anyway. I've been called rebellious, contrary, too independent. But, lo and behold, you have to be like this to get over a stroke. My personality is good for something.

BEING BAD
FEELS
SO GOOD

make a supreme effort to not look like I had a stroke. This means moving faster than I am really comfortable with, not staggering, not falling, not shaking too much, doing things neatly with that left hand. But sometimes I catch a glimpse of myself in the mirror and see, horror of horrors, that my head is waggling. I instantly hold it straight and still, but, truth be told, it feels so good to let my head waggle. When I'm tired, keeping it together feels like being in a straitjacket.

This doesn't exactly give you incentive to appear "normal." It gives you incentive to give up, actually. It gives you incentive to say, "screw it," and waggle all you want. This feels so good! Trouble is, you won't get a lot of respect this way. In a world where outward appearance means so much, it's a ticket to being treated like...a toddler. So when you're with people, *don't waggle.*

No matter how much effort it takes.

For the tenth time, I'm learning to walk without a cane. Because when you use a cane to help smooth your walking, people read all kinds of things into it. *You must be old.* (Strokes are instant old age.) *You must need a lot of help.* (You do need some help, but you don't need everything done for you.) *You look disabled.* (This is personal; some people like being disabled.)

But as time goes on, I find I'm getting a bit fed up, too. I'm almost at seven years; I should be cured by now, right?

That is another problem I have! Expectations, expectations. Everyone else seems to think that it's been so long, my disabilities must be permanent. I think this way, too. Yet, in my heart of hearts, I know I can improve. Keeping motivation up is hard, however.

I notice people who have *specific* motivations tend to get back to normal faster. Like that tennis pro I met in line for the movies. How did he recover so fast? He wanted to play tennis again. Likewise, doctors are motivated to get back to their medical practice, and pianists want to get back to playing, even though they must relearn their coordination, and so on. If you find out quickly how to adapt, as I did, you'll always be disabled. Which means I have to start typing using my right hand again. Read aloud each day. *Notice what makes you a little better. Keep doing it, even though you may not see much progress for a while.*

This is so hard to do, because what works is uncomfortable, feels wrong, and you just plain can't do it.

I rebel at the thought of being a forever freak. Yet progress takes work, grit, and determination. Moving up to the next level is not as simple as waving a wand. I wish it were! I'd be the first in line! Wave that wand, buster. I don't feel like walking 3 miles every day.

Someday, they'll have a pill for this. In the meantime, I have to work so hard it can be exhausting. And ... some of us are doing the same things over and over, even though they don't work. Time to change it up! *Try something different.* At the very least, you might find something else you can't do.

EATING
IS NEVER
THE SAME,
EITHER

B less my caregiver, Delia. Not only was she a great cook, but she cut up my food for me into bite-sized pieces. So I could eat it. She did this so well that I didn't notice. That is, until she left, and I had to figure out how to eat on my own.

At first, I only ate things I could fold up and chomp on, like pizza, and things that didn't require cutting, like tuna salad. But then I had my first dinner party. I made a roast beef and had someone else carve. All was well until I looked at that slab of meat and realized I couldn't eat it without looking like—a caveman. Juice running down my chin and all.

Everyone was chatting, laughing, praising the food, and I picked delicately at my potatoes. Until the woman seated next to me realized something was wrong and asked, "Do you want me to cut up that meat for you?" I felt like hugging her but refrained; she cut up the meat, and I gratefully ate it up. It was delicious, probably doubly so because I'd been given access to it by a kind stranger.

It's amazing how you can adapt. I got along for years ordering only those things off a menu that didn't require cutting, including hamburger.

The problem was, when I went to someone's house for dinner, I had no control over what they were serving, and it often did require some cutting. I'll never forget the first time

I had the courage to attack chicken, off the bone no less. I took a deep breath and tried using my right hand to cut. I missed, and the chicken went skittering across the table.

The tablecloth was a mess, and I was mortified. My hostess was very gracious, put the piece of chicken back on my plate, and cut me a few slices. I ate them demurely and left the rest. Better to starve than to send that poor chicken to the other side of the table again.

This was followed by about another two years of only eating things I could handle with a fork. Then one evening, a delectable-looking steak was put in front of me, and I was hungry. By now I had a little control over that right hand, so I used it to jab my fork in and cut with my left hand. It wasn't graceful-looking, but it worked. I managed to cut two-thirds of the steak this way. I was so exhausted afterward that the bit about resting after dinner finally made sense.

Yet I was also triumphant. I cut steak! Such a small, simple thing, but try doing it with one good hand. This is what I mean about avoiding all those things you can't do. I wish I could say I did it every night from then on, but I still avoid food that can't be eaten with a fork.

I've been reaching up and washing my hair for years, and it's gotten marginally better, but my right hand still shakes and has little control. I'm sure my hair is cleaner on the left side.

Now that I'm writing about it, I'm ashamed that I haven't made more progress. I will eat my pizza tonight with a knife and fork, civilized fashion. I'll do it in the kitchen, where the damage will be minimal. Otherwise, there will be pizza all over the walls of the house. And it's really hard to get out tomato stains.

WHY IS
RUNNING
SO HARD?

I n my dreams, I run. In fact, in my dreams I am just like I
was before. Does this happen to you? I am told there's a
difference between natal disability, the kind you're born
with, and acquired disability, the kind you have after misfortune strikes. Like a stroke. Or a heart attack. (There's a
reason why doctors refer to strokes as "a heart attack of the
brain.")

I am constantly comparing what I used to do without
thinking about it, with what I can do now.

It's not that I haven't accepted the stroke, there's just a
certain level of frustration where there didn't use to be. I
used to move very fast, without ever thinking about it, and
now I move slowly, and if I don't think about it the price is
very high.

So today I tried, in my front hall, to run. Now, I can't
run, but I found I can walk very fast without falling. This
is a pleasant surprise. And maybe tomorrow it won't work.
But it set me to thinking: maybe the barrier is that you don't
think you can possibly do it. Maybe you just have to try. And
try again.

I don't mean to keep harping on this, but think about it
for a minute. I reached a certain stage, and believe me it was
hard-won, and I thought I couldn't do any more. I could. I
just had to prioritize at this point because I couldn't be all

over the place like I was in the beginning. I had to decide, *is running more important than typing with my right hand?* Because if I tried to do both, I would do neither. So I set one goal and stuck with it.

After I walked fast up and down that hallway a few times, I was tired. I stopped. Now, if I stop for good, it'll remain a pipe dream. I've had plenty of those. Somehow, I have to learn to do it.

Good news! The next day I took a long walk with the dog (keeping my hips still) and concentrated on walking a straight line. I'd say that I was able to do this 60% of the time. That's some kind of small victory.

OTHER
SERIOUS
ILLNESSES

I keep saying, and you keep reading, stroke, stroke, stroke. What if you haven't had a stroke, but instead have another serious illness? Heart disease, maybe, or kidney failure. Losing a limb, or your sight. A terrible auto accident. Or perhaps you've just been diagnosed with MS, or lupus. There's so much that can and does go wrong with the human body, it's a wonder that anybody is healthy and whole.

Everything I've said here can and does apply to those situations. Your life has forever changed after your diagnosis. Nothing will ever be the same, because you've tasted your own mortality. Likely you'll be a much better person, although it's hard to see that early on, when you're just focused on what you have lost.

It's like joining a club that you never wanted to join. *Oh, now I'm one of those people. The people I've always felt sorry for, when I even noticed them.* You know what? You *are* one of those people, only now you get to see it from the inside out.

It's stunning at first (Breakfast with Idiots, anyone?). Then you gradually get used to it. Eventually, you see it as an advantage. I can't hurry the way I used to, but hurrying is not such a great thing (unless you're in a crowded theater and somebody yells "fire!"). Your illness or accident is going to teach you so many things, some of which you never cared to learn. You'll learn despite yourself.

In some ways, no one will ever understand, because to them you may look fine. You may have had a heart attack and made a full recovery. You, and your life, look hunky-dory. But you'll never forget that terrible day you fell to the ground and were rushed to the hospital, where great doctors saved you. It could happen again!

One of my favorite stories involves a guy who had a heart attack and died before he was revived by a level-headed friend who knew CPR and was standing next to him when it happened.

"The day before, I'd had a routine check-up," he said, "and the doctor told me I had the heart of a guy half my age. I was so proud. And within twenty-four hours, I had a massive coronary and died."

That guy will never be the same. He's joined the club. Only someone else who's been through a trauma will truly understand. You don't want to dwell on it, because that will cripple you far worse than any illness. But it's good to know some of those people. They understand where others, no matter how sympathetic, never will.

Tackling
Taxes

Three years after my stroke, I tackled my own taxes (with the help of TurboTax). I figured it was about time. I couldn't walk a straight line, tired easily, and was dizzy as all get out. But my cognitive abilities hadn't been affected by the stroke, and I'm stubborn. So I attempted them.

My taxes weren't complicated, but I had disability income streams. I had enough of them that even now I can't remember what they all were. 1099s were put who knows where. My taxes were probably pretty easy to do, but I managed to make them complicated. An accomplishment I'm not proud of.

To do my taxes properly, I had to open a filing cabinet and take out the papers I needed. Easy, right? The problem was, I was so dizzy that each time I bent over the files, I had to concentrate on not falling down instead of pulling out the papers I needed. Mistake number one.

I figured out that if I sat down, it would be easier to pull open those drawers. Kneeling was actually the best way to do it, but for me that was out of the question. I swayed way too much.

I discovered that even if you are not cognitively affected by your stroke, you might be in some kind of a fog. Forgetful and disorganized. In the best of times, I'm not exactly great at dealing with paperwork. This was not the best of times.

I did my taxes as well as I could. I remembered something a former boyfriend used to say: "Arrogance is the art of going wrong with confidence." I definitely went wrong with confidence.

A few days later, I looked over my tax return before sending it to the IRS. There were some areas left blank that I thought shouldn't be. This worried me, but not enough to prevent me sending it out as it was. Can you imagine—I thought the IRS wouldn't care that I didn't complete everything I should have completed.

I realize now that I had just left those areas blank *so I could come back to them later*, when my brain was fresher. I never did that. I just licked the stamps and put it in the mailbox (this was before one could file electronically, which I currently do).

The IRS, being slow, took a couple of years to send me The Letter. By which time I had forgotten the whole thing, but they hadn't. I owed them money (duh), plus penalties for underreporting, plus tax for not paying enough taxes. I handed the whole mess over to an accountant, who did that year's taxes all over again, and spent a lot of time on the phone with the IRS. They wouldn't budge, so I had to pay back taxes plus all that extra money in penalties (more than I owed in taxes) in installments. I have used that accountant ever since.

The moral of this story? *Don't do things you are not ready for.* It should have been a big clue when I saw those blank spaces, but it wasn't. Also, *don't mess with the IRS.* They don't kid around, nor are they sympathetic even when you have a real, documented, brain issue.

Now, after eight years (my, time flies when you've had a stroke), I'm about to try TurboTax again. Unless I chicken out and use an accountant.

It burns me up that people like Warren Buffet pay less than I do, but this is not a book about politics. If there's one thing I've learned, strokes don't care what your ideology is. They strike indiscriminately, killing some people and rendering others disabled to some degree for life. And not able to deal with the IRS.

PART FOUR

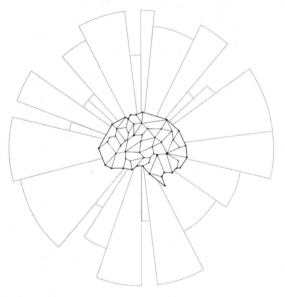

PANDEMIC? WHAT PANDEMIC?

There's a global pandemic going on as I write this, and I would be remiss if I didn't mention it. COVID-19 has everybody on edge, and most people are more or less staying at home. Only grocery stores, drugstores, and hardware stores are open, and people are wearing masks to those. It looks like a bunch of bank robbers are perusing the shelves, but people know better and are cutting a wide berth around shoppers. I am as suspicious as anyone else.

I say all this with great irony, as those with decreased mobility pretty much live like this all the time. Lost your job? I feel for you, I really do, but I lost mine for good six years ago. In danger of losing your home? I am truly sorry, but after my disability ran out, I had to sell mine. You are suddenly poor? Welcome to the club. I was making good money when I had my stroke. Then all of a sudden, it was all gone. I lost some friends, too, who just couldn't handle my illness. I don't blame them, mind you, and the friends I've kept are as wonderful as ever, but stuff happens. Life changes. You have to adapt.

Now the world is crumbling around me, but I see a lot of positive things happening. Families are spending time together, and the kids are so happy to have their parents around. Air pollution is way down, as is the price of gas. You can drive and park. The ozone layer is already thickening up.

Animals are breeding like crazy and in many cases overrunning new developments that took away their favorite places to do whatever it is that animals do.

COVID-19 has been a blessing in disguise, but some people don't see it that way. They think life was great before and can only see what they've lost. Those are the people who won't do well getting over a debilitating stroke. You lose a lot. If you can't see what you've also gained, well, you're going to have a problem.

Stroke is about loss and it's about making those other things that have not been lost important. Physical people might want to take up wheelchair racing or playing basketball from a chair. Anyone can do it! Nonphysical types will find that books and movies will become best friends. Socializing will be that much more enjoyable when doing less of it.

As a stroke survivor, you get to stop and smell the roses. If you can bend down that far without falling over.

HOSPITAL
ETIQUETTE

haven't been in the hospital for a while now, and believe me, it's no great loss, but someone (maybe me) should write up some rules of hospital etiquette, posted at the front door:

1) *Thou shall not complain to the nurses.* I was horrified to hear patients endlessly whining and treating the nurses like their personal servants. Stop! These hard-working people have your best interests at heart. They do want to see all their patients get better and get released. Cut them some slack.

   I have a great nurse story. Seeing how restless I was, some nurse who shall remain nameless snuck me out onto the deck where only hospital employees were supposed to be. I sat in the sunshine, looking at trees and mountains, feeling like the Queen of Everything. It was a very bright spot in an otherwise bleak day. I'll remember it, and think of that nurse fondly, for the rest of my life.

2) *Shut up about the double room.* Unless you're rich, you'll have a roommate. (I could write a book about roommates.) *You are not the only person in your room.* This means that your crying relatives are not going to make your roommate feel any better. Neither are making noises during the night, murmured conversations that go

on for a long time, endless complaints—about the way you're being treated, the medications you're taking, the food. The food will always be bad—although one hospital I stayed in had a Mexican chef who really knew how to cook. Flavorful tidbits showed up on my tray at every meal. Kudos!

3) *Don't have pizza and chocolate next to your bed.* That poor person next to you is going to smell it. You wouldn't want a starving urchin by the window while you were eating restaurant food, would you? If you don't intend to share, don't do this.

THE BODY
REBELS

Who would ever have thought that your body would betray you? Yet when you have a stroke, that's exactly what happens.

Your mind commands, "Lift that hand," and your hand stays in your lap. *What the—* you think. What's going on? So you repeat it. "Lift that hand," thinking maybe the hand didn't hear you. But it stays stubbornly in your lap. What's going on? There's a wall between what you're thinking and what your body is doing, that's what. And it's going to be harder to take down than the Berlin Wall. There is no Gorbachev to intercede on your behalf.

This is where either the rubber hits the road or it doesn't. Most people give up at this stage. And why not? Parts of your body just won't behave, no matter how many times you tell it to.

For instance, I just finished ironing, something I detest anyway, but I just couldn't put it off anymore. The clean, wrinkled clothes were piling up. And ... whenever I lifted that hot iron, my hand shook. Dangerous. In fact, every time I put the iron down, I said a little prayer. It must have worked, because I didn't scald or burn myself.

You see, I'm part of that stubborn minority who just doesn't give up. Are you? To read all the books about strokes, you would think that trying again and again results in ... success!

In a year or two! Well, some of us just aren't so lucky. There are no quick cures for us. There's just years of slogging to make a little progress. In the meantime, you have to live your life. You can't let the stroke take over, because at some point you have to let go of it. Other people will. They'll wonder why you don't if you don't let go of it, too.

Recently, and without any work on my part, my voice changed. I no longer sound like a cartoon character. The pitch has come down. I heard myself talking recently, and I was surprised. I guess my vocal chords are relaxing a bit.

I've been talking, hesitantly and with a high-pitched whine, for years now. Not practicing, just talking as I need. What does this mean? I'm not exactly sure, but I think it means just what I've been saying from the start. The more you do something, the more chance you have of improving. Strokes, like trains, are on their own timetable. Just because you think you should be better by now doesn't mean you will be. It will happen in its own way, in its own time.

Just as the 5:15 isn't going to come at 5:07, you're not going to get better one minute before your body is ready to. As my friend said, "You have to learn every letter in the word patience." I think I'm now up to the *t*.

FEMALE STROKE
OR
MALE STROKE?

This sounds like a silly question. Until you think about it. Why should strokes be different from other parts of life? As you're treated differently when, say, you're applying for a mortgage, you'll be treated differently when you have a stroke.

One of my most vivid memories, and one of the first, was of learning again to do laundry (I didn't like it to begin with). I was in the rehab hospital, where they had moved me after a week. I stared at that washer and dryer thinking, *really?* I was still in a wheelchair, couldn't walk, couldn't talk, and they had me doing laundry? I looked around me. No men in sight.

I asked the woman who was wheeling me around why I was being taught to use a washer and dryer (which I already knew how to do, believe me). She blithely told me it would come in handy soon. Clearly I'd asked the wrong person.

The second day at the same rehab hospital, I learned to wash dishes. Again, I was disbelieving. We may smoke slimmer cigarettes (actually, we don't smoke at all), but we haven't come very far. "Do men learn these things, too?" I wanted to know. I upset everyone by upsetting the apple cart. Men probably don't even *think* about these things. For them, they don't appear on the radar.

I don't know if there are statistics for this, but I'm betting men recover better and faster because it's assumed that they will want to *do things*. Women are such hothouse flowers, we must be left alone to lick our wounds. Not me, I'm not a wound-licker.

As a woman, some of it is pretty good. Later on, when I could contemplate going to Starbucks, young men all got up and held the door for me, some of them even carrying my coffee outside for me. I'd be lying if I didn't say how much I appreciated that. Later still, men helped me load up my trunk in parking lots, and boy did I appreciate that. I needed it, actually. And I was aware that if I'd been a man, chances are good it would never have happened.

Men who have strokes are usually eager to get back to whatever they did before, and so they have greater incentive to recover. Lifting heavy packages, moving boxes around, being "handy" around the house, all good things, but they require strength and dexterity. Hard to do when you are weak or paralyzed on one side! Yet men, for the most part, learn. Athletes tend to learn really fast, because they have highly developed muscle memory on their side.

This is not meant as a treatise on the differences between men and women—it's just that you'd better know that you'll be treated one way or the other. I had to fight like the dickens to learn certain things, like getting in and out of a car, because women just don't worry about those things. They'll always be "helped," because they are helpless, right?

I wonder if men learned to do laundry and dishes as part of their therapy. It sure helps with dexterity. But you know what I really loved? Playing baseball with a plastic bat and ball! Talk about learning hand-eye coordination! And I found it so much fun. Too bad I only got to do it once or twice. Too bad no therapist noticed how much I was laughing and having a good time. But I got to do laundry and wash dishes lots. Although I hated it and was silent and glum the whole time I had to do it.

Why, oh why, don't therapists realize these things? Why do they typecast you right away? Why do they force you to do things you dislike? I really don't want to be told that "time doesn't matter," then have a therapist stand over me with a stopwatch.

Some women actually enjoy doing laundry and dishes (please send them to me right away). Some men balk at the idea of being handy, but they are natural geeks whose eyes light up when they see a computer. Whatever, you are probably going to be typecast when you're getting over a stroke. This is detrimental to everyone, especially the person who had the stroke.

If you're not scrappy, you're toast. I didn't ask for that baseball bat again, but I should have. Live and learn!

Seven Years
and
Counting

Today is my anniversary again. Seven years. It's a dubious achievement at best, but I figure I'm here for a reason. Maybe writing this book is it.

I celebrated by going to Lowe's and buying uninteresting things. Light bulbs. A new bird feeder. That kind of stuff. It felt strangely good to come home with nothing to speak of; but I got some things out of the way. And when I walked in the door, there was no rush to see how anything looked.

No rush. If anything is a theme here, there's no rush for those of us who have had a stroke. We know we're going to die, so that isn't the big deal it is for many others. We can't get excited about it. It's just another fact of life.

Way back in year one (and that seems about a million years ago now), my doctor told me that he knew a woman who'd had a stroke twelve years before and was still improving. Horrified at the time, I'm now so glad to think about it. Because no matter how many years it's been, three or five, twelve or twenty, there's always room for improvement, and you are never really finished. So don't think that if it's been fourteen years and a kind of stasis has set in, you have gone as far as you can go. No sirree, you haven't. Not by a long shot.

The other day a friend sent me a YouTube video of herself in an exercise class for people in wheelchairs. No big deal, you think, people in wheelchairs have been exercising for decades now.

And at first I thought the same thing. I watched it fondly and speculated on the upper body strength those who are wheelchair-bound must have. Arm muscles! Shoulder muscles! Muscles upon muscles! As one who has never been particularly muscular, this awed me.

Then the light bulb went off. My right arm and leg have not been well coordinated since the stroke. I have a form of aphasia, no doubt due to the vocal muscles on my right side not working properly. But what if I just exercise the right side? What if I do the calisthenics, to driving dance music, only on my right side? It has to be less frustrating than learning, again, to touch type with both hands. Or hitting a ball against a wall, only to spend most of my time chasing it down so I can start again. "Do what you love" is great advice, but what if you can't do it at all?

So from now on, I'm going to practice calisthenics with my right arm only for about ten minutes each day. Can't hurt, right?

I've found that as the years wear on, I'm less and less motivated to try what I know I can't do. Yet I won't get anywhere without that motivation. What a Catch-22! How can I get that fire in the belly again? Only by being confronted with something new that I really, really want to be able to do but can't. Or not well, anyway.

Finding that motivation means developing an openness that you never had before. Other people can get complacent, set in their ways, but not you! It's the kiss of death if you've had a stroke, and excuse the analogy. (I've already been kissed by death.)

This is what separates stroke survivors from most people. Maybe I'd rather be like most people. I'm so sorry to tell you that train has left the station. It's just too late.

I find that you can never be complacent when you've had a stroke, no matter how long it's been. If a battle plan isn't working, do something else. I can't tell you how excited I am to realize there is a new thing for me to try, something that might work. I'll let you know!

LOOKING FOOLISH— DO YOU DARE?

I know I've touched on this, but now I want to go into it in greater detail. Because the more courageous you are, the better your chances of getting better.

I'm at eight years and one month now (but who's counting, right?), and I still can't walk properly. My voice is rather thick, my tongue moving slower than I can form words, and I still have trouble with the *rst* and *rld* combinations. (*First* is hard! *World* is not much better).

I still hesitate for a nanosecond when I have to speak to store clerks and waiters, also when I have to make a phone call. What if they don't understand me? I have learned that people want to understand you. And if they don't get what you're saying, you can always say it differently or spell out a word you're having trouble with.

One of my friends, a great cheerleader if ever there was one, is always reassuring me that I'm easy to understand, my walking is better than I think, I've pretty much overcome my problems with my right hand. (Although people look horrified when I forget and try to use that hand quickly. It shakes wildly.)

My point is, if you're waiting to be perfect before you make your debut, you'll be waiting for a long time. Maybe for the rest of your life.

Remember Breakfast with Idiots? I've come a long, long

way since then, but I'm still visibly disabled.

In the beginning, I drooled. My hair was two different lengths. I couldn't even think about putting on makeup. My face was probably lopsided, as I had my stroke on one side. (My left side recovered completely years ago, my right . . . I'm still working on it.

If you're ashamed for one minute of anything your stroke left you with, I'm here to tell you that I would not have gotten so far if I weren't willing to look foolish. Also, other people would not have had the chance to know that disability is nothing to be ashamed of. One day it might happen to them. I'm such a good role model!

I found this out in a completely unexpected way. I attended a class where one other student (among about twenty people) had multiple sclerosis. She was severely disabled but spunky as all get-out. Smart as a whip, she had also traveled quite a bit, although I could see it must have been hard for her. By the end of that class I had only admiration for her and what she had done with what life had given her.

Just think . . . she must have learned a lot along the way! If I had never practiced walking, I'd never have learned how to walk. If I had never practiced talking, even though I had aphasia, I'd never have learned to talk. It's so hard, especially early on. You have to learn that if no one understands you, you've just got to try harder.

It's not my fault I had a stroke. It just happened to me. I may wish it hadn't, but I could have done nothing to predict it or lessen its effects. It's that simple.

I can be a good example. Be bold. I can take the dog out for a long stroll. Don't let someone else do what you, with a little extra effort, can do for yourself. Your bank account, insurance company, and you will be happier.

LARGE
MOTOR SKILLS
VERSUS
SMALL
MOTOR SKILLS

When I was a child, I became obsessed with a game called jacks. Some of you may remember this (ahem). The game involved throwing a bunch of star-shaped objects on the floor, then bouncing a rubber ball and picking them up at the same time. Bounce, pick up a jack, catch the ball. Bounce, pick up a jack, catch the ball. Keep repeating until all of the jacks have been picked up. Then try picking up two jacks, three jacks, and so on. Play as many times as you want (for me, this was dozens of times).

I didn't know it at the time, but I was learning many valuable things. Hand-eye coordination for sure. Manual dexterity (those jacks went everywhere, including under the furniture). Delicacy, because sometimes the jacks landed right next to each other, and I had to pick them up one at a time. Speed, because that rubber ball came down really fast, and I had to be done with the jacks and ready to catch it in time. Dexterity, because I had to hold onto the jack and catch the ball with the same hand.

Whew! That's a lot to keep track of. Yet I practiced and practiced and got really good at it. Why am I telling you this? Because as children we have so much patience and always have our eye on the prize. That coordination and dexterity serves all of us very well for our whole lives. But it becomes problematic when you have a stroke.

My right side was affected by the stroke I had, so forget about jacks, which I always played with my right hand. In fact, I have trouble doing anything that requires small motor skills on my right side. So my right hand is pretty good at hauling heavy things, helping pick up packages, large motor skill things. When it comes to moving a coaster from one side of the table to another, it gets dicey. I have to pick up the coaster, clumsily, and drop it somewhere else. I position it more carefully with my left hand.

Today I bought a new keyboard, well aware of the fact that I'm typing with my left hand only. I knew I needed that keyboard no matter what. But it's a small motor skill item, and I'm not anywhere near good enough with that right hand to use it the way it was meant to be used.

I hear there is a professor in Alabama that invented something called CT. He has you put a sling on the good hand, only using the one that doesn't work for just about everything. This seems to me a very good therapy, but highly impractical. How are you supposed to get anything done that way? At least for the first few weeks, maybe more.

I am trying to be able to shampoo my hair using both hands. I hit myself in the head a lot, but slowly I'm learning to do this. It's a small motor skill, but it's one of the things I can do without breaking or dropping something important. You have to find these everyday things to learn with, or you won't develop small motor skills. Unless you have a set of jacks and a lot of patience.

THE
VOICEMAIL
MESSAGE

Sooner or later I had to do it. Put a new message on my voicemail. What should I say? How should I say it?

You can avoid this for a while in any number of ways. One of them is to just keep using your old message. People will listen and either think, "Well he/she is doing better than I thought" or "I see that he/she hasn't changed the message. Poor thing."

Once upon a time, it was no big deal to record a personal message. Unless you're picky like me, most people just do it and never give it a second thought. Maybe they even forget to record something and don't bother about it.

If you have some form of aphasia, now it's a real problem. You want to be understood for sure. But you also don't want people thinking you've reached normality, because you haven't.

You can always have your spouse or a member of your family record the message. I left my old message up for a while, then used the official one that came with voicemail. You know—the one that's so generic you don't know if you've reached the right number or not. I just couldn't record my voice, it sounded so bad. Like a cartoon character on steroids.

Fast forward a few years. My voice had improved to the point where I could carry on a conversation without having to figure out how to say every other sentence differently. So I recorded a new message.

Years ago, someone called me "a cute pain in the butt." I chose to focus on the cute part, not the pain in the butt part. This came back to haunt me when I recorded my first message. Because *it didn't matter how cute I was.* It mattered how I sounded, and that part was definitely not good.

So I practiced and practiced. Wrote my message down so I didn't have to remember anything, just read well. This must be how actors deal with a script, until they know the lines. I got to the point where "Please leave a message" was becoming a mantra.

All this for two little sentences! I recorded them over and over, thinking that I didn't sound so bad. I could be understood at least, as opposed to the gibberish I produced before.

Finally I reached the point of exhaustion, so I hit "Save." Done! Have I listened to my message? No, but no one's complained about it, either. Good enough for me. The picky one.

Perfectionist
No
More

When you've had a stroke, you also need to have an attitude adjustment. At least I did. You have to let go of a lot of things, or think of new ways to do them. Look at the Special Olympics! All those athletes figured it out.

The other day, I saw a woman riding a bicycle with two wheels in the back, culminating in a big basket. I was so intrigued I stopped her and asked about it. Turns out she has balance issues, but she loves her bike. The basket is for her dog.

Now, that bike is tailor-made for me, and I live where it's flat, so I don't have any hills to worry about. It's hot, too hot to ride during the day, but I could take a spin after the sun sets. I'm still thinking about it, but I don't have any excuses. It would mean I could ride a bike again!

Everyone has a goal in life, or a few goals, and this is one of mine. I love bicycles and want to ride one again. It sure is a good answer for not being able to walk for miles, as I used to. If you don't have to watch traffic (that's a big "if" these days), a bicycle is a great way of being outdoors for a long time, and seeing a lot that you miss when driving or riding in a car. (You see a lot when walking, too, unless you're concentrating hard on getting from Point A to Point B.)

On paper, there is no reason why I can't at least get a

tricycle. This is a great example of overcoming looking foolish (a tricycle, *really*) and overcoming fear (what if I fall
down? And on cement, no less).

The people who recover the best are afraid of *nothing*.
The people who recover best *don't care what they look like.*
What won't you try because you know you can't do it? If
you've had a stroke, perfectionism will get you nowhere. I'm
guilty of perfectionism, and it's holding me back. If I could
get over this, I'm sure I would improve by leaps and bounds.

TALKING ON
THE PHONE

Herro, it's Eireen." No, I'm not Irene, and what does "herro" mean? Let's try again. "Hi there, it's Eileen." (I can manage this.) "Is Merry there?" Whoops! I meant to say Marie. But the person on the other end seems to know what I mean, so she fetches Marie. Whose name I still can't pronounce correctly.

Marie (not her real name, but you know, the lawyers are happy about this) and I have a long chitchat, during which I notice two things. One, I talk slowly, and as soon as I try to speed things up, my tongue just can't track the words. The other is that, in a few minutes, I'm tired. A lot of work goes into a few sentences.

Lucky for me, Marie is very chatty and I don't have to say a lot. "Listen to you," she marvels. "A year ago, I understood only about half of what you said!"

It's true I've come a long way. But after seven years, I thought I'd be speaking just as I did before the stroke. Is that going to take another seven years?

I asked my eldest brother if I once had a lisp. He is taken aback by the question, but says, "No, you never did. Even as a toddler." *But I do now.* It's kind of embarrassing to be an older adult who can't speak properly. Three-year-olds often speak more crisply than me. And they never even have to think about it!

I speak better when I remember to enunciate, and exaggerate my facial movements. Which is a recipe for wrinkles, but, given the choice, I'd opt for speaking clearly. I once met a woman who'd had a stroke, and you needed to talk back and forth for at least ten minutes, and listen closely, to hear how she faintly slurred her words. I hope to get there soon. I'm already at the point where I can have very brief conversations and people don't realize I have trouble speaking. Now, that's a novel goal.

If I were a speech teacher, I would give myself a homework assignment: read out loud for an hour a day. For one thing, I would learn to speak for a long time without getting exhausted, as muscles and stamina improve with use. For another, I would speak more crisply, I hope. I've never persevered enough to really know, I'm sorry to say.

Did you used to read your children bedtime stories? Time to revive that habit. *Goodnight Moon* needs you, and you need it.

PEOPLE
GO
FAST

They're actually normal, you're the slow one. But rushing isn't the answer, either; that's when you fall. There really isn't a good answer that I know of.

Remember slowing down for your grandma, or your son or daughter when they were little? Well, guess what—people slow down for a stroke survivor. (Ever have someone grab your arm and hustle you across the street before the light turns green? I rest my case.)

You have to be sensible and only expect people to do it for short periods of time, those periods well spaced out. Because, when you're capable of much more, which most people are, it's like being in prison.

I have discovered that when I talk slowly, I pretty much can pronounce everything. And everyone understands me. But I get impatient. Like a slow driver, when everyone's passing you by, I think things would be great if only I could talk faster. My tongue does not agree.

When I try to talk fast, I become all too aware that my tongue just cannot keep up. I start slurring my words and mispronouncing things. Worse, I just don't pronounce certain syllables because they're too hard. All the progress I've made in talking goes down the drain. People start saying "what?" again, and I have to repeat myself.

Just like in the old days, right after my stroke. Do I want

to go back to that? No, I don't.

I've read enough about aphasia to know that it's a long way back to talking normally, and most stroke survivors don't make it. I'm guessing that some people give up when they realize how hard it's going to be. You have to ask yourself, do I want to spend the rest of my life scribbling on paper? I doubt it.

Communication is so important. Besides intelligence (and sometimes you have to wonder about that), it's what separates us from animals. (No snarky comments about many animals being better than people—I know that.)

You need to learn to communicate, no matter how slowly you have to speak. The speed will come later.

Now, walking is another matter. Most of the time, it doesn't matter how slowly you walk. But sometimes it does. For instance, I have moved to a place where it rains a lot. So what, you may think. So... I can't jump over puddles, and I can't race home if it starts to pour a half block away from my front door. I just can't! My body won't move that fast.

I've become resigned to getting wet a lot.

Some of my friends go running in the morning, and I would love to join them. I'm sure they would love that, too. I just can't move that fast.

Most things take me three times as long to do. Getting ready to leave the house, for instance. If you think finding your keys takes a lot of time normally, try doing it after you've had a stroke. Stroke survivors know what I'm talking about! Putting your shoes on can take forever. Making sure the house is locked up—that going from room to room checking windows and doors can take several minutes. The list goes on and on.

If you try to do things faster, there will be a high price to pay.

As I was a very quick person, this is very hard for me. I will probably always be slower than I'd like (that isn't diffi-cult, believe me).

The thing you have to learn, *I* have to learn, is that people would rather you be slow than to have to call 911. When you think about it that way, you'll forget about being fast.

STROKES
AND
CLIMATE
CHANGE

There's no correlation, right? One has nothing to do with the other.

Of course a stroke has nothing to do with disappearing ice, rising seas, hot temperatures, wildfires. (There's a lot more to climate change, but it gets depressing to list everything that's happening.)

However, a stroke greatly impacts the ways in which you *react* to these things.

If you're flooded out, or there's a tsunami, can you get to high ground fast?

If there's a tornado, can you run to a safe place?

When a wildfire erupts, and you have minutes to leave your house, are you ready? Can you scoop up your pet, get in the car, and go?

I'm haunted by the news stories, during Hurricane Katrina, of hospitals and nursing homes in New Orleans scrambling to react quickly enough. And the only reason most of those people survived is the knowledge and dedication of the nurses who took care of them. Heroes, all.

But what happens when danger strikes and there's no one to help?

Even a few years ago, this was a moot point. I had my stroke at the end of May 2013. Things were relatively calm then. Now the news is, almost daily, full of natural catastrophes that often strike with little or no warning. Since you can't move fast, often can't think fast, and may often be left alone . . . what to do?

I used to live in the San Francisco Bay Area. I was there for the Oakland hills fire. Over and over again, I heard my dentist tell the story of getting his family out alive. The frantic phone call from a neighbor. Looking out the window and seeing the fire engulf his neighbor's house. Seeing his own roof catch a spark. He herded his wife and children, all in their morning bathrobes, into the car and headed down the hill. In his rear view mirror he saw his roof exploding, his house going up in flames. Then he hit a traffic jam and thought, *we're all going to die in the car*.

Somehow, he got the car down that hill with everyone in his family alive. They lost everything and had to start again from scratch. "We didn't even have underwear," he said. But they rebuilt their house and started life again.

Could I do this?

Recovering from a stroke takes all the resiliency any patient has got. Yet in certain circumstances, one will need more.

This is distressing to think about, yet like most negative things, it's got a silver lining. Many stroke survivors, like me, want to live in relative safety. This is a chance to relocate. *Because you can't move that fast. And you don't have endless stamina.*

Where you choose to go is up to you entirely. But climate change is happening all over, and it's happening fast. It's especially difficult for us stroke survivors. In fact, it's kind of like a double whammy.

Older people might want to take their chances, wherever they happen to be. That's understandable. But I have decades to go, so I'm thinking about it more seriously. Because I don't want to hamper anyone. I want everybody to be safe. Or as safe as anyone can be.

Disabled
for Life, Part I

It's said (who said it? I don't know) that a third of patients who've had a stroke make a full recovery within a year, a third make a partial recovery that's ongoing (I put myself in this category), and another third don't recover at all. Everything depends on the severity of your stroke and which part of the brain was affected.

After a year or so, you kind of know what category you're in. But even then, there are skills that don't fit neatly into those categories. Relax. You're not the only one.

I supposedly have aphasia. I don't speak crisply and clearly, and I get tired of talking after a few sentences. Yet I have no trouble reading, and I don't forget or reach for words. I perfectly understand everything I read and hear. These are all classic aphasia problems, but I don't have them. The only thing affected was my speech, and I'm working on that.

I conclude that the part of my brain that controls language was affected—but only up to a point. And, as I've come a long way from talking gibberish, I'm making progress. Not nearly fast enough, if you ask me, but progress nonetheless.

Here's the kicker: people who have had mild strokes respond to therapy fast and make a lot of progress in a short time. But . . . most people who have had strokes are in the other two categories. How do you reach them? Are there special therapies for us? Should we follow the same therapies as those with mild strokes, but more intensively?

No one has real answers to these questions. For every Jill Bolte Taylor, who had a pretty severe stroke but made a full recovery, there are several hundred (maybe several thousand) people who do the same things but seemingly make no or little progress. What's the difference? Does it lie in their personalities, the people surrounding them, their therapists? Or is it a function of the brain and where they had their strokes?

No one really has the answer to this. I can tell you that my speech therapist was right out of university and didn't know what she was doing. They invented the word *inexperienced* to describe her. I'm sure she was very inexpensive. But she was also very ineffective, and I made almost no progress with her. Surprise, surprise.

Likewise, my occupational therapist, although quite experienced, was sick of her job and made no bones about how anxious she was to get out of the hospital and home every night. She was a clock watcher, and it should come as no surprise that I made no progress with her, either.

My physical therapist, Bret, was not only all there but loved his job and was full of energy and optimism, not to mention creativity. If one thing wasn't working, he would try another. My secondary physical therapist, Marilyn, was a lot like Bret, only, as can be expected, more maternal. I made amazing progress with those two. I think experienced and dedicated therapists are very important. Who knows where I would be if my speech therapist and occupational therapist had been as good as Bret and Marilyn.

This isn't a plea for National Health, but hospitals are so cheap and bureaucratic, it's a wonder anybody gets lucky with therapy at all. Some therapists regard themselves as merely having a job, and are happy to collect their paychecks and go home. You may be disabled for life mostly because of them. This is a heavy responsibility. But it's real.

I don't want to take anything away from the therapists who are wonderful and often work miracles. But, as a stroke survivor friend said, "You have to be your own therapist." (Certainly this is true after your insurance runs out.)

There you are, as vulnerable as a newborn baby, with things wrong with you that you can hardly fathom, and you find yourself at the mercy of a Russian roulette of care. You are shocked to find that some people in the health profession just want to dismiss you ASAP, whether you've made any progress or not. If you don't take matters into your own hands, you'll be disabled for life. How scary is that?

It's taken me seven years to go from severely disabled to being, as a friend put it, "a little disabled in some ways." I'm working on not being disabled in any way, shape, or form, but if I didn't have the determination and grit it takes, if I ever gave up, well, I wouldn't have made much progress at all.

Disabled for Life, Part II

What does it really mean to be disabled for life?

I'll always have that placard for my car that marks me as disabled. Or a disabled license plate. Even though the blue parking spaces are almost always taken. (And they're almost always in the sun. Don't parking lot designers realize that disabled people don't like to get into a hot car, either?)

I'll forever see *that look* on people's faces when they have to deal with me. You probably know which one I mean. They can be the kindest of souls, but they'll always talk to me in a certain way. They can't help it.

Some people will not have known you, or remember you, when you weren't disabled. Recently I moved to another state and I realized *no one knew me before this happened.* Here I'll forever be the woman with disabilities.

Everyone has a story. Mine will always be that I had a stroke and I'm now *disabled for life.* For some people this is okay, for others, not.

When do you accept it? When do you make the decision that it is not acceptable, that you'll always keep striving for the next level? This is very personal. But I keep thinking, if I don't keep striving for something better, I'll just stay where I am. Forever.

Remember, I'm the one who got up from a wheelchair

and learned to walk. Because I didn't want to be the person who was in a wheelchair. It's a pain in the neck, and very limiting. I wanted to walk, to drive. I now do both. I have even started taking yoga classes. My balance is iffy, and lots of the standing poses are beyond me. But someday—someday.

MY
CANE

I have a love/hate relationship with my cane. It gives me
stability when I need it, and sometimes I do need it. New
places, long walks, tree roots throw me for a loop. I'm glad
to have my cane on the occasions when I have to deal with
those things.

But sometimes I leave the house and find I've forgotten
it. You don't have to be Sigmund Freud to figure that one
out! Truth be told, sometimes I just don't need it. But I like
to carry it around with me. You never know. There might be
a tree root up ahead.

I have also found that canes are psychological. If I have
it, I feel confident. I can tackle anything! If I don't . . . suddenly I'm not sure I can get across the street. Distressing
but true.

Recently I was horrified to find another use for the cane.
(No, I didn't use it to kill a snake.) Without it, it seems, I
have to prove that I'm disabled. With it, people are respect-
ful and don't ask questions.

What? I'm the same person. But without the cane, I look
much better. Stronger. Younger, even. So people treat me
accordingly. What's she caterwauling about? She looks fine
to me.

So my cane has taken on new meaning for me. It's a
symbol, now—that I'm still disabled, still have balance that

needs improvement, still can't move as fast or as well as "normal" people. Hold up! Here I come!

It's kind of shocking, and an unfortunate whiff of the real world. I'm striving hard to someday be normal, but does that mean I'll be treated as a throwaway? Will people refuse to help me when the perception is that I don't need help?

This disabled thing is a double-edged sword. If you're *too* disabled, no one will want to go near you for fear of doing something wrong. If you're not disabled at all, well, you can take care of yourself, right?

My doctors are fond of *gray areas*. "You're on the spectrum," they tell me. "But you're not really sick. You're not well, either. Somewhere in between."

This is how disability goes. You have to be *somewhat* disabled. But not too disabled.

This brings me back to that cane.

One of these days, I'm not going to need it anymore. Right now, closing that front door without taking my trusty cane seems impossible. But one day . . . I simply won't need it anymore.

You may be eager to get back to work of some sort, and my hat's off to you. I'm getting around this by writing this book. *I'm writing a book*, I say. Because really, I have to do *something*. Besides teeter across the street.

All of this disappears when people see that cane. So if you find yourself going backwards, remember I said all this. Getting well truly is a double-edged sword.

STROKES
AND
COVID-19

If you haven't noticed, we're having a pandemic right now. People who have had strokes will say, "Welcome to my life." Because we're used to having restrictions, so in some ways this is easier for us.

Then the TV tells me that COVID-19 causes tiny blood clots in some people, blood clots that can lead to stroke. In young people. This is not amusing. I have no idea if the strokes are as small as the blood clots, but they may need to read this book more than most people.

Strokes are often thought of as something that pretty much happens to the elderly, and they don't count anyway. They're going to die soon anyway, right? Just like those most susceptible to COVID-19! But strokes *do* happen to young people, too, and even if you're older, you may have ten, twenty, even thirty more years to go. This is like getting "long" COVID-19 when you're, say, 38. You have the rest of your life ahead of you, but at any point you can have respiratory issues, a stroke, brain fog. Maybe all three. And vaccines, while very effective (in my estimation) might not protect us against future variants.

What to do? While we're all waiting for a cure for stroke you can finally treat yourself like the fragile thing you really are. This means that you should put yourself in the high-risk group, because, seriously, do you want to be battling a potentially lethal illness as you're struggling to recover from something else? It's hard enough to deal with a stroke. Imagine dealing with the aftermath of a stroke AND recovering from the new coronavirus. No, thank you.

COVID-19 can be boring, but you already know about boredom. If you must go out, wear a mask and use that hand sanitizer liberally. As hard as it may be, try to stay away from younger people, because apparently they think they're immune and like to hang out in bars and such. You simply don't have that luxury. Good books and movies will become your mainstay. I retain my sanity by gardening. Pulling weeds is a great antidote to feeling like I'm stuck inside, which I am. I can garden to my heart's content; it will improve my balance. And maybe fix the side that doesn't work.

Who's afraid of COVID-19? All stroke survivors should be. At the moment, I'm living in Florida, hot spot extraordinaire for the virus, so I have to be extra-careful. This gets tiresome, but it would be even more tiresome to be fighting to breathe in a hospital. Your family cannot come to visit! If you die, you die alone, as even the nurses won't touch you. I don't know about you, but I find that a nightmare beyond comprehension.

The moral? Picture dying alone in a hospital every morning when you wake up, and don't get sick. There are some things I can still do, even when I don't particularly want to pull weeds. I can still take long walks outside. I can still talk on the phone or have FaceTime chats with my friends. I might even become a birder, because all I need is the great outdoors, a good book, and a pair of binoculars. If I go out by myself or with a trusted companion, it's safe.

No one expected this pandemic, except maybe the infectious disease experts. It's a real pain, but you know what? People like us are uniquely suited to it, and you can't say that about most things.

PART
FIVE

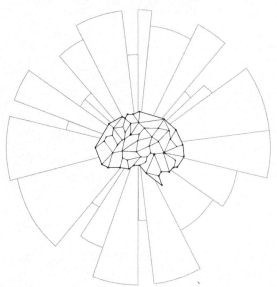

MAKING
PEACE WITH
YOUR STROKE

Strokes are a funny thing. I don't mean ha-ha funny; I mean can't-figure-it-out funny. In point of fact, neurologists spend almost a complete lifetime trying to figure out strokes, and they don't have a clue. How can I?

It's been seven years for me. For some people, it's been twelve, fifteen, twenty years. For some, only a few months. Yet everyone is asking the same questions: Where will I end up? How long will it take? Will I ever be normal, or close to normal?

I was asking these questions years ago. I'm still asking them. Doctors, nurses, caregivers all have given me the same sorrowful look. They don't know the answers. It depends on me, on how hard I want to work for how long. Even that changes! When I wake up in the morning, I no longer think, *how can I improve today? What can I do to go to sleep tonight feeling that I've done everything I could?*

For most people, having a stroke becomes a balancing act. (Never mind that your balance isn't so hot.) You need to make your peace with what has happened and feel good about yourself anyway. This is not so easy when you're around other people and can't keep up, but you have to do it. *This is where I am for now. Good for me!*

On the other hand, if you don't keep trying to get better at things, you never will get better. I've started, for the twelfth time, to read out loud in the hopes of improving my voice. Guess what? I get winded after a couple of pages. But I've also noticed that I can now pronounce multisyllabic words, something I could never do before. My *Rs* are improving. I can now pronounce *R* at the beginning of a word. Rabbit. Reconfigure. Robust. Those words don't scare me anymore! My speech therapist's admonishment that my tongue shouldn't touch anything and I shouldn't use my lips *(What? You're kidding, right?)* suddenly makes sense. When I do it right, my tongue isn't touching anything and I'm not using my lips at all.

My point is, I'm not beating myself up about not pronouncing my *Rs* correctly. It's one of those incredibly frustrating contradictions. Just when I came to accept that I never would pronounce *R* again, I started to do it.

Some women will tell you that they couldn't get pregnant until they gave up and adopted a baby. There's something about that giving up that makes you suddenly able to do it. Don't ask me why, or how.

The other thing that happens after a while is that no one notices the little improvements except you. I'm not getting a pat on the head for being able to pronounce multisyllabic words. A friend said recently, "You know, I hardly ever have to ask you to repeat things anymore." Chances are we've both gotten better—me at pronunciation, she at understanding me. Better, better!

There are some things it may take years to figure out. In the meantime, I have to accept, accept. It's like accepting that you have curly hair. I know people who are still struggling with this even into old age! Some people will die never having accepted it! This is so sad.

You have to love those out-of-control legs before you can make them calm down. Does that make sense? So easy to say, so hard to do. Try. You might surprise yourself.

In the Beginning, I Drooled

This may seem horrifying and even disgusting, but the vast majority of people do it and have no idea where it comes from.

Everybody drools. Dentists and hygienists can tell you that. Ever get several shots of Novocain in the side of your mouth? You probably drooled. People think nothing of that, or they even find it funny, because it wears off pretty fast. The dentist tells you, "Don't eat soup or drink anything hot," so you don't. Until the meal several hours later, when the shots have worn off and so have their effects.

If you've had a stroke, you're either paralyzed on one side or, like me, out of control. The saliva puddles in your mouth, but you can't swallow it fast enough, or properly, so you drool.

The drooler, in this case me, is mortified, but I couldn't do anything about it. Until I got better.

Drooling does not mean you're an idiot (Breakfast with Idiots notwithstanding), it just means you have little or no control over your speech, your breathing, or your saliva. When you're at the drooling stage, you might want to give your helpless bystanders a little treatise on drooling. They'll be impressed, and they'll never look at drooling the same way.

Now, I almost never drool. In fact, I only do it when I have a coughing fit. I'm prepared for this, so I always have a tissue handy and no one sees anything except some woman coughing into a tissue.

If you drool and find it mortifying, it definitely helps to understand why you do it. You're not trying to gross out other people. (Although sometimes it feels that way.) As you get better, the drooling goes away. At some point, it disappears.

But as with most other things, there is a price to be paid. As a layer of self-control returned, as my behavior got more and more "normal," I lost that lovely feeling of having no inhibitions at all. On some deep level, I enjoyed being more of an animal.

Soon after I came home from the hospital (times and dates were fuzzy then), a friend of mine sadly died quite young of ALS. I insisted on going to his funeral and burial. Big mistake, but what did I know?

At the funeral service, which was held in a big Catholic church, I started sobbing loudly. Whatever friend took me (I don't remember that, either) successfully shushed me into silence. But I resented the fact that many people were as sad as I was, they just knew how to control it. The animal in me rebelled.

At the burial, I couldn't walk to where the casket was lowered into the ground, so I stayed in the car. And cried. Jill Bolte Taylor might have commended me on my lack of ego, but I should have stayed home. The friend who died would have understood.

Today I'm like anyone else when it comes to emotions (sorry, Jill). Early on, there are so many things you can't control. Drooling is one of them. Emotions are another. For better or worse, a layer gets stripped away. Maybe it evolved to be protective. I know that when it started to come back—and that took about three years—I didn't want it. In fact, I felt desperate about it. No, no, no! Somebody help me! I felt like a superior being, and maybe I was. But in the end, the self-control wins and comes back. Now, I'm horrified at the thought of life without it. Then . . . not so much.

STROKE STORIES

That old saying is so right: *Nothing is certain in life except death and taxes.* I had my stroke in late May 2013, so my taxes were done and filed for 2012, but the next year some wonderful person did my taxes, and I have no idea who. But they were done and filed on time, and until recently (I clean out my files once in a while), I had all the paperwork to prove it.

I don't know what happened the year after, either, but my taxes were done and filed on time. Again, by someone. I took over the third year and screwed them up royally (I've made my peace with the IRS over this), and after that I have used an accountant.

Now my head is entirely clear and I feel ready and able to take over this task again. Actually, I've been ready for three or four years. It's a huge milestone.

A neighbor made sure I owned my house. Many people have unusual circumstances, and I am no exception. At the time of my stroke, my former live-in boyfriend, who was in another state by then, was still on the deed to my house as a tenant in common. Those of you who are familiar with legal matters will understand what this means, but unfortunately, I didn't. So when a neighbor who was a real estate agent knocked on my door one day, having just found this out, I didn't know why she was so upset.

"Just think about it," Ganice pleaded. "If anything happens to you, he owns half this house. I don't care what private agreements you have (we did; I had paid him off), a judge will look at one thing: his name is on that deed."

I argued with her for a while, but she was adamant. I had to get back his half of the house. I had to be the only person on the deed.

I figured she knew more than I did, so I finally acquiesced. She handled all the paperwork; all I had to do was show up and sign. And it was a good thing, because truthfully, I wasn't capable of anything more than that.

I did have to get in touch with my former boyfriend (luckily I had his email address) and get him to make a long drive to sign papers, but within about three weeks it was done.

Thank you, Ganice. You are one of several people who took care of what needed to be taken care of. The moral of this story is *Have your life in order*. If you're like me, this is a royal pain, but you'll be so happy you did it.

Ganice was helpful, but not everyone is. I'm telling this to illustrate how people can become different from what you remember and how you have to watch yourself all the time.

Every night, I took the dog out for a short walk, just to the end of the block and back. I could, with a lot of vigilance, manage this. But I lived on a hill, so the end of the block was down a steep sidewalk and back up again. The sidewalk was narrow, too. (I have since moved.) Charming to look at, but difficult to navigate.

One night, I encountered two women I knew with their big dogs, both dogs lunging at the ends of their leashes, women and dogs filling the sidewalk. They could have moved into the road, but they didn't. They saw me teetering with my little dog and just kept coming toward me. So I had to pass them on that narrow sidewalk.

I was pretty upset about this, so I fell, luckily on grass in someone's yard. One of the women came to see if I was okay, but I sent her packing, got up and continued my walk. The moral? *Some people have an agenda you can't see. Know who your friends are.*

THE WORLD
IS NOT
UPSIDE DOWN

There is a song from the Broadway musical *Hamilton*, "The World Turns Upside Down." It was written to describe the chaos after the American Revolution. But it's a great way to characterize what happens after a stroke. Your world turns upside down.

Years later, I can think clearly, make decisions, and take care of myself. But let me tell you, it takes a village. If you're lucky like me, many people will pitch in and help in whatever way they can.

I say, let them. Let people do what they're good at and what you need at the moment. They'll feel great, you'll feel great. Know that one day you won't need this, but until then, thank your lucky stars that you have those people around. I did. They are precious.

PERSONALITY
TRAITS
COME BACK

When you've just had a stroke, you're reeling, emotionally and physically. A filter has been removed, maybe the ego, so that you feel things more, are quicker to get angry, quicker to forgive. You may think, "I've been changed forever." Well, not really.

I thought that same thing. I had no appetite and lost a considerable amount of weight. Everything tasted bad to me. Chocolate bars piled up because I simply didn't have any interest in them. All the things I loved to eat—good bread, pasta, salads—elicited no more than a shrug.

I was more than happy to eat whatever my caregiver felt like making, and only a few bites at that. I was gaunt as all get-out, to the point where I scared even myself, but guess what? It all went away.

I'd say it lasted three years or so. Gradually, my appetite came back. It started innocently enough, with my stomach rumbling and me realizing with surprise that I was hungry. Hungry!

Today, I love chocolate again, pasta, good bread (which is increasingly hard to find). I make delicious salads almost every day. I have gained weight, about fifteen pounds, and no longer look like a scarecrow.

Plenty else reverted. That emotional filter came back, to my chagrin. Aware of it, I fought it every step of the way, but that is one battle that I lost. Too bad, because I think I was a better person without that filter. We'd all be better people without it, frankly.

The stroke knocked out any other disorder I had, and now they're all back. What does this mean? Can the body only fight one thing at a time? I prefer to think that when you really let go and have only one piece of stress in your life (the stroke), everything else disappears. What does that say about the way we live? Can we fight disease with much less stress? I don't have answers, but I wonder.

Insomnia went away. Whereas I used to toss and turn and wake up for two hours or so in the middle of the night, after the stroke I slept like a baby. I slept a lot, in fact! The difference—everybody expected me to sleep a lot, even during the day, so I did. I slept so much you would think I had sleeping sickness, but I had no problem falling and staying asleep. Those old-timey pictures of men sleeping on the beams of New York skyscrapers 100 stories up? That was me.

The first time I had insomnia again, I knew I was on the road to recovery. Even though insomnia is a bad thing. That's what I mean by it all comes back. Things you wish *wouldn't* come back *do*.

The hours you would normally keep come back, too. I've always been a night owl. Even as a child, I kept the whole family up with my after-hours antics. My favorite was singing loudly while everyone else was dead tired and falling asleep. I, however, had tons of energy.

There was howling from the other bedrooms and cries of "Be quiet and go to sleep!" Till I had the stroke, I could still run around the house doing things at one in the morning, but after...that was a different story.

All of a sudden I was awake at 6 a.m., ready to start my day. And I started yawning by 9 p.m. What had happened? I don't know, but I changed to the point where my hours coincided with everyone else's. Which made them very, very happy.

I don't know when it started to change back; it was slow and gradual. But now I go to sleep at around 11 p.m. and get myself up around seven-thirty or eight to walk the dog. Sleeping nine hours is normal to me. I don't understand people who say they get by on four hours of sleep. Really? I would feel as if I were in a sleep-deprivation experiment. I could easily go back to going to sleep at 12 midnight and getting up around 9 a.m., but I already know what it's like to be out of sync with the rest of the world.

What else? After the stroke, I stopped caring about my appearance. Makeup? What's that? Clothes that match? Who cares? Now, once again, I care. I actually hold up my tops against my pants, thinking, does this go?

Styles came and went, and I hardly noticed. But now I do. Luckily I dress classically, so very, very few of my things are trendy to begin with. But if something is hopelessly out-dated, it goes out.

Driving was something I had to get back to gradually. For the first couple of years after my stroke, I didn't drive at all. I would look at my car parked at the curb and think, *no way*. But one day I looked at the car and wanted to drive it. But I hadn't driven in two years, plus I'd had a stroke.

I found a lovely friend who was willing to teach me to drive again. Of course, I knew what to do, but my driving skills were rusty. He drove to an abandoned naval base where there was no traffic, and I practiced. Turning left and turning right. Parking every which way. Backing up (that was the hardest). Practice, practice, practice.

Today, I drive the way I always did—like a bat out of hell. Oh, I was so sedate for a while! What happened? It all came back, that's what happened. This is a good example of being better off if some things don't come back. I was a slower, more careful driver back then. Now? I'm sure I look per-fectly normal behind the wheel, but taking fewer chances would be great.

I lost interest in reading after the stroke, but now I read a lot. I lost interest in writing. Now I'm writing a book, and many of my emails are gargantuan.

I could go on and on. Because really, I lost interest in most things, some of which was fine with me. But it all comes back.

I don't feel like the same person, but I don't know what my friends and family would say. Maybe I've come fully back, I don't know. But change, normally so hard, is easy after a stroke. And the changes feel permanent. Which is why it's so shocking when you find out they aren't.

Following a stroke is a great time to get rid of your addictions, because you really won't care. And it's easier to never have them come back than to have to fight them to begin with. It's a great time to lose weight and keep it that way. Exercise? You'd better be slow and careful about that, and check with your doctor first.

Which leads me to something I'd nearly forgotten about. I practiced yoga for almost twenty years, greatly improved my strength and flexibility, but thought, after my stroke, that I'd never do it again. To my surprise, four years after, I took a Gentle Yoga class and loved it. Because of my balance issues I need to hold on to something when others don't, but still. I'm doing yoga!

Now, seven years later, I've taken two Pilates classes. They are much harder because everything's so fast, but I'll bet I can keep up in a few months. And . . . it's good for my balance. That's what I tell myself, anyway, as I clutch the barre.

Balance. I'm still frustrated, but then I remember that a year ago getting from the car to the front door of a store was a challenge. It doesn't scare me anymore. It's *still* a challenge, but I know I can do it. That's one change that I welcome.

The Joys
of
Having
a
Caregiver

Some guys, unless they live alone or have a very egalitarian relationship, may already have a caregiver. She's a wife, or live-in girlfriend. She does the cooking, cleaning, laundry, keeps track of schedules. If you're not handy, she also does, or oversees, the handyman chores.

But for women, it's a luxury and a wonder to have someone else do everything. Put breakfast in front of you every morning, and then clear the table. Help you dress. Take you for a walk. Cover you with a blanket when you take a nap, which is often. Make sure your walker works, which often entails putting tennis balls on the ends of the shafts. Bring you your medicines with a glass of water, which also gets whisked away, cleaned, and put back on the shelf.

Why do people complain about their caregivers? Yes, they're human, and sometimes they're late, and sometimes they have an alcohol problem. But they are great companions, attentive to your every need. They watch TV with you, whatever program you want. They're quiet when you're sleeping, which is a very big deal, indeed, especially when you need a nap every two hours or so. To some people, myself included, all this solicitous attention comes as a revelation.

Caregivers listen patiently when you practice reading out loud, do puzzles with you to help get your cognition back on track. My caregiver also supervised my exercises, helping me get up and down.

In fact, a caregiver is a combination of nurse, cheerleader, and mom. Just when you really need that. Like Mary Poppins, they magically appear at your door. I had a bad two hours when I first came home from the hospital, when my brother left to catch a plane and before my caregiver arrived. I was alone for a very short time, but I was scared, and normally, I'm pretty fearless.

Like a dog, I knew I couldn't survive on my own. Then the front doorbell rang, and my life changed instantly. Eventually I found a great caregiver who lasted a year and a half and who slept in the guest bedroom most of that time. She appeared at my bedroom door if she heard any noise coming from me. In the middle of the night, even. Like a friendly ghost.

Until I could fend for myself, which was a slow and gradual process, Delia did everything. On the rare times she couldn't make it, her daughter-in-law took her place. Another honey of a person.

We underestimate what these people do. Maybe some people are lucky, and their caregiver is a close relative. It helps if they have experience with strokes, because then they will understand why you sleep so much and why every little thing tires you out. It also helps if they go home at night. You have to watch that neediness thing. It's all too easy to become very dependent on your caregiver.

I haven't needed a caregiver for years, but now I smile when I see an elderly person with a caregiver that obviously has become a friend. That is the best thing you can hope for. It doesn't always happen, but when it does, it can be very sweet, indeed.

BREAKING
BONES

've had some setbacks for sure. Therapists warned me about this so apparently it's pretty common. And it's a good thing I was told, because otherwise I would go nuts wondering why my right hand seemed better just a few months ago.

Stroke survivors also often break bones. Those are *big* setbacks.

We break bones because we fall so much. Most of the time, we're just black and blue. Most of the time, I twist around and fall on my butt, which is pretty safe because I have enough padding to ensure that I don't break anything. This may be the only time I've ever wished my butt were bigger.

But sometimes I'm not quick enough. That's how I broke both my leg and my hip. Separately. At different times. I can shake my head at both incidents now, but at the time they weren't funny. Not at all.

I broke my leg first. I was out walking the dog, and she saw a squirrel or something. For a couple of seconds, she was so wild that, although I had her on a leash, I lost control. Not only of her, but of myself. Down I went, one leg under me. I thought, *I've really done it this time.* Little did I know how bad it was.

I had to crawl to a stop sign to haul myself up by its post. I could not put any weight on that foot. Every time I tried, the pain was so great I nearly blacked out. I was three-quarters of a mile from home, and I didn't know how I could get there. In fact, I didn't know what to do.

Lucky for me, several women had seen me out their front windows and now came running out of their houses to help me. One of them got her SUV and drove me home. Another took my dog and followed. They all offered to help further, but by that time my tenant had come out of my house and took over from there. Somehow I got into his car, he put the dog in the house, and he drove straight to the nearest ER.

Oh, no! I thought. *I'm in the hospital again!* The leg throbbed, but there was no swelling and everything looked perfectly fine. Which was good, because *there was no doctor on duty.* This was a big hospital in a major city, and I had to wait—and pay for—several hours of just lying there. If we want to fix our health care system, we can start with that.

The attendants took an X-ray, of course, but there was nothing they could do because there was no radiologist on duty, either. I may as well have gone to a local store, because I would have received better treatment.

After almost five hours, an honest-to-goodness doctor showed up and pronounced my leg broken. (No kidding, Sherlock.) But guess what? There was nothing he could do, either, because I hadn't been formally admitted to the hospital. At this point, I wanted nothing to do with them, even though it was a new place, beautiful and gleaming—but clearly they didn't have their act together. I had the simplest of problems, and no one had any time for me or knew what to do. I had no faith in them whatsoever.

I wish I could say there was a quick fix, but a simple broken leg turned out to be a big problem. No hospital in Oakland or Berkeley could deal with me, it seems. This was not a rural area where they had few doctors and no hospitals. It was a big urban area where you couldn't get decent medical care, it seemed.

It took a week and a few private appointments to get anything done. I went around with a broken leg, in a lot of pain, for a week. That is hard to believe. Even harder, after I found an orthopedic surgeon who promised I would get well really fast if I had a titanium rod put in my leg and my M.D. wouldn't approve it. Now I can't blame her, because I probably didn't need it.

I had to wait for a week before I could have the surgery, and I had to beg and plead with my doctor to okay it, which she finally did. But it took three doctor visits to do this, so I was driven around, with an untreated broken leg, for a week until I got approval for treatment. *In this day and age.*

I probably would have done better with a vet and a splint. At least I would have just hobbled around for a month while my leg healed. By the time I had the surgery, the pain was subsiding and I could put a little bit of weight on that leg. It might have healed nicely by itself.

The surgery was mercifully short, but the hospital (in Berkeley), had *no room for me*, so I was put in the basement, which was like a dungeon, until I could go home. The first night I had to pee so often, I kept apologizing to the attendant, who had amazing good humor about the whole thing, even though I was getting up every half hour and needed help getting to the bathroom. I dared not tell my friends where I was since they had come to the hospital so often after my stroke. I didn't want to make them come again! For two days I saw nobody except nurses and attendants.

It was not fun.

Folks, I have words of advice: make sure you live near a good hospital with good doctors. You may never need it, but if you do, take this as a cautionary tale. I am not known for my shrinking violet personality, but in this case my protestations fell on deaf ears. My handicap did me no good. I was simply ignored, something a sick or injured person should never be.

To return to this juicy story...

Because one side of my body was weak and shaky from the stroke, I couldn't use crutches, so I wore what I called "the boot," a black contraption I had to wear on my leg for two weeks after surgery. It was heavy and awkward, but no heavier than a plaster cast would have been, and at that stage I didn't feel like complaining. I was so happy to get home, I didn't complain about much of anything!

You'd think I'd never do *that* again, but about two years later, I was walking the dog—again (poor thing, she is being blamed for so much that isn't her fault)—and I fell, hard (is there such a thing as a soft fall?). I tried to twist around so my butt would take the brunt of the fall, failed to do it in time, and broke my hip.

This time, no one came running out of their houses. A car or two passed by, but no one stopped. I had moved to another town, another neighborhood, and I questioned my sanity. Amazingly, *I walked home.* I didn't know, at that point, that my hip was broken, but I was in excruciating pain. And I had my dog in tow.

Somehow, I made it home. I dragged myself up the stairs (cursing them) and plopped down in an armchair. Curiously, being seated brought no relief, which should have been a clue right there. The Tylenol was upstairs, and I did not want to walk up another flight of stairs, so I took no painkillers, although my hip was killing me.

An hour later, when I still didn't feel any better, I decided to go to the Urgent Care Center. I was so new to the area, I didn't have a doctor yet. No one is pleased when you don't have a doctor, because there's nowhere to send test results. Note to self: *When you move, find a doctor right away.* It's way more important than getting a library card. Or a new license plate.

The Urgent Care people were just lovely, but after they took an X-ray, I found myself in an ambulance heading toward—you guessed it—another hospital. This time (new town, remember), the experience was much better. I got a real room, with real sunshine, and a great nurse. Again, my roommate was questionable (a dying woman who didn't speak English), but I managed.

I spent four days at that hospital, then went home where I was confronted by those stairs. I made it up to the main floor, then slept on the couch until my hip healed. The good news: insurance pays for more therapy, and for more social workers. But I had to heal, again.

I wish I could say this was the last time I fell and hurt myself, but it wasn't. Fast forward another three years or so when I was living in Florida, clear across the country. I went to a nearby mall because it was air conditioned, and I fell again in Crate and Barrel. I don't know why I fell. I can only think it was a combination of polished concrete floors (very slippery) and me turning around fast to check out something that had caught my eye.

Down I went. This time, I was using a cane. This time, I didn't have time to break my fall. I fell flat on my face, and was I ever a mess. I cut up my lip something fierce and lost a tooth. (Well, it was wobbly and the dentist extracted it.) I fractured my nose. I was bloody and dripping plasma. I looked bad!

You know those movies where the hero gets beat up and looks good in a few days? Don't you believe it.

I healed in a couple of weeks on the outside, but not on the inside. Although I looked okay, I was in the middle of replacing that tooth and wouldn't get my permanent implant for another two months. Meanwhile, I developed a healthy fear of falls and am extra-careful now. Which must look great, but I figure being careful all the time is better than falling and maybe ending up in the hospital. After my last fall, I didn't need a hospital, but I spent a lot of time in the dentist's chair, repairing the damage.

All of which points to . . . chances are a stroke survivor is going to fall a lot. It's not just me—I hear it from stroke survivors all the time. If you're lucky, you'll just get bruised. If you're not so lucky, you'll break bones. Or fall on your face.

How do you minimize this? If you have the answer, I'd love to hear it. Maybe there's a trick that I don't know about.

I've reached the point where falling seems impossible; I feel that healthy and well balanced. But every once in a while I lose all sense of direction, my right knee freezes up, and I know that I can fall and hurt myself. It's always totally unexpected and unpredictable. That's scary!

Relaxing
to
the Nth
Degree

M any years ago, before my stroke, I went to a chiropractor. It was something to do with my feet, I don't remember exactly. He worked on my head and neck (a lot of good that did me), and kept coaxing me patiently to let go of tension. I tried, but most of the time I didn't succeed.

A friend of mine who had several strokes went to see a chiropractor and said he really did help her. He loosened her jaw so she could speak more clearly, and it worked. She only went for a couple of sessions, but I imagine if he had more time to work he could have done more. First, of course, you have to find a dedicated and knowledgeable chiropractor, and for some that might be a challenge. (I've always found that personal recommendations by those you trust work the best.)

I now think of the very nice woman I see in a wheelchair who was pushed by her husband. Her right side was pretty much paralyzed, the hand permanently clenched into a fist. I'm willing to bet she knows exactly what to do with that right side, but her brain won't let go.

What if, by some miracle, she could? What if she could unclench that hand enough to practice using it? Her problem, really, is one of letting go.

My right side was affected by my stroke, too, and I'm

still learning how to use it properly. I notice that when I can make it relax, the shaking nearly stops. When I walk, my right leg hits the ground much harder than the left, which operates at a whisper. It throws me off balance, so that gets affected, too.

When I can relax and just *let go*, I can be almost normal. I can do it for several seconds now, a big improvement. Eventually, I'll be able to do it for minutes at a time. And still later I'll be able to do it all the time, but I can't even think about that now.

Marilyn, one of my physical therapists, used to tell me, "You don't have to kill it." Meaning, I do way too much on my bad side. I'm still repeating this to myself as I still want to overdo. No need to stomp when I can walk gently. No need to clutch with that right hand when I can hold with a fraction of the strength.

My brain has learned to overdo. Now I need to learn how to just do. You can't get over a stroke and be a control freak. You have to get over the latter in order to have a chance at the former. Not the greatest news for many of us, but there it is.

Do less, and you might be able to do more.

HEALING
IS A
LIFETIME
PROPOSITION

'll never forget how horrified I was to hear my brother casually say, "I have to make sure I get enough sleep. I get tired more easily than other people." He had had his stroke—caused by an auto accident—fifty-eight years ago. That's right, fifty-eight years.

He got back to "normal" in a couple of years, but I saw residual effects for years after that. He had to give up his chosen career and find a new one. He had a normal life, got married, had kids, a house—the whole nine yards. Yet the stroke has haunted him his whole life. He's just not quite like other people.

I know another woman who had a stroke, hopped out of bed a few days later, and seemed to have had no effects at all. Yet a couple of years later, she noticed she was falling a lot. Her balance was somehow off.

If I do too much for too long, the dizziness comes back. It took me years to get rid of it in the first place, so you can imagine my horror at feeling it again. I didn't think it was possible! But it dawned on me that I'm always going to have to watch myself. This is not good news, but this is my reality.

When I was a child and walking to school, I occasionally met up with a girl who'd had polio, the disease of the day back then. Her legs were in braces and she didn't walk all that well, but what she lacked because of the polio attack didn't affect her guts and determination. I admired her, even in a time when people were indifferent to her plight, or worse, dismissive of her and of the disease (which was merciless). But...I'll bet she's still fighting.

This can happen to anyone, and it may be hard to avoid freaking out. Strokes can do a lot of damage, and some of it may be unseen and unfelt at first. When rebuilding those circuits in your brain, they are more fragile than the original ones. But it can all be managed. I got rid of the dizziness by resting up for a couple of days. If I hadn't...who knows what would have happened?

The key, I learned, is knowing how much I could do, and when I needed to stop. This could be hard, especially when my friends were staying up till the wee hours, and I wanted to join them. Instead, I had to learn to excuse myself and go to bed earlier. Probably for the rest of my life I'll need to monitor this.

Not fun! Not fair! But stop and consider the alternative. I don't want to backslide to the point where I need to learn something all over again. I've already experienced the decision to go back to a cane when I thought I was done with all that. It was, truthfully, not fun and not fair. Now I can walk without a cane, but I almost always have it with me, just in case. It's good for scaring away aggressive animals, I can tell you that.

It's kind of embarrassing to have to tell somebody you like that you can't spontaneously run around with them that evening because you've had a full day. But I find that if I say, to hell with it, and do it anyway, I'll pay a very high price. Better to be momentarily embarrassed.

Am I going to have to be this way for the rest of my days? Probably. Just as some people have to always manage their diabetes, and they check their blood sugar levels quietly and discreetly, I'll always need to quietly and discreetly deal with the after effects of my stroke. It isn't that big a deal.

By the way, an uncle (a different one) of mine has had diabetes for decades. He always took it seriously and watched his diet. He just celebrated his 90th birthday. Which goes to show that you can live a long life after any debilitating illness, but you'll always have to be a little more careful.

I'm
Too Old
to Get
Better

This is a tough one. Having a stroke at, say, 98, may mean this may actually be true. But if you're 90 or younger, you may be too young to think that way. You have to take it on a case-by-case basis.

Since I am decades younger than 90, why am I saying this? Because I met a guy who was 89 and had just had his first stroke. The first thing he told me was, "I'm improving every day." I met him *at a gym*. Working out. And looking terrific.

Because if you have a stroke at, oh, 84, you may live into your late 90s. Would you really want to spend all those years not improving and setting that kind of example for kids, grandkids, maybe great-grandkids? Or would you rather fight back?

Many people feel they are too old to spend years getting better. It takes a lot of time and, often, unbelievable effort. To that I would say, "Do you have anything else to do? Is watching Netflix more important than improving after a stroke?"

Maybe for some it is. I know I can't talk because I'm not at that age yet, but I have a feeling that if you're a fighter, you're a fighter at any age. Take my uncle, for example, the 98-year-old. At 93, he was a little distraught that doctors discovered his heart valve was leaking. A small amount.

And because of his age, surgeons wouldn't operate to give him a new valve.

Some people would just shrug and think, *What can you expect at 93?* But my uncle was *pissed*. Something was wrong with him! Since he's still kicking at 98, six years of a leaky heart valve is clearly not affecting his longevity. Although he's smiling, you can bet he is *even more pissed off*. He's a fighter.

So for someone who has had a stroke late in life—should they just roll over? If there's longevity somewhere in your family, it may be well worth it to exercise, take walks if possible, and improve, improve, improve. If you're a fighter, you'll do this anyway, but even if you aren't, you may have a lot more years to go. It will be worth it in the end.

What!
You're Not
On
Autopilot Yet?

Autopilot—it's like the Holy Grail for stroke survivors. In the first year after my stroke, my therapist told me that eventually—there's that word again—I'd be on autopilot. It's been seven years, and I'm still not doing things carelessly, thoughtlessly. I thought by now I'd surely be accomplishing everything automatically.

I never thought I'd yearn to be mindless, but here I am, yearning to be mindless. I can't even imagine how it would feel to walk without thinking about every step. Without thinking, *Now you're losing your balance again and going right to the edge of the road. Or, Your right leg is still shaking, that's why you rarely put it down straight.*

I can't imagine reaching out my right arm without thinking, *Don't knock that glass over.* (Sometimes I'm too late.) I'm just starting to slowly mop up messes with that right hand. At least I rarely hit myself in the face anymore!

There are moments—and they're coming closer together now—when I forget everything and find, to my surprise, that I do quite well. Then there's the morning, when I first get up. I'm wobbly, so I have to go slow. The bathroom seems very far away, although in reality it's just a few feet. I hang on to the bedpost for the first few steps. But . . . the bed and the room no longer spin while I'm stationery.

I long for the day when I can spring out of bed and sprint

around the bedroom. Will it ever come? I don't know, but I hope it does.

In the meantime, I do everything slowly and carefully. Actually, yesterday I grabbed the dog in play, very fast, and I promptly fell on the rug. The dog was as surprised as I was. Much more upset, too.

I can move relatively fast when the doorbell or the telephone rings. The other day I heard my brother's voice on the answering machine and was so proud that I reached the phone, picked up, and started talking before he hung up. A first! But I wasn't on autopilot.

I'm still surprised when I start speaking and the words don't come out as if I'm reading them—crisp and clear and fast. Will they ever? Will I be able to talk on autopilot instead of thinking about how to pronounce every word? And then still having it come out wrong anyway?

Being on autopilot means you are doing everything perfectly—or nearly so—to begin with. Then you don't need to think about it. By that measure, I've still got a way to go. But there are those moments... tantalizing glimpses into future possibilities. I like to think, *I will get there.*

GIVE UP
OR KEEP
STRUGGLING?

reached a point where I wondered if all of this was worth it. Maybe it wasn't. Why should I keep struggling when I'd made peace with my stroke, and I was managing to get along? Maybe not just fine but fine enough?

This is such a personal decision, one I go back and forth with. From the time I wake up to the time I turn off the light and go to sleep, I can do almost everything I need or want to do. I change the sheets. Make the bed. Get dressed. Walk the dog. Decide what to eat, three times a day and cook, bake, or shop. Write. Exercise. Read. Drive, sometimes as long as five hours, which was always my limit before the stroke. Dust and vacuum. Hang pictures.

I could go on and on, but the point is, while I can't run, skip, jump, ride a two-wheel bicycle, I could easily stop now. I could just cry Uncle and live the rest of my life this way. My family and friends are used to it. I don't fear strangers anymore, because I can be understood. Why put all that unpleasant effort into speaking crisply, walking smoothly, using my right hand? Not shaking at all?

I've had this conversation with my friend who has had several strokes. She's a pleasure to talk with, and we can shoot the breeze happily for quite a while. But I can't help but notice, when she first gets on the phone she sounds almost normal. Then she deteriorates.

Is this okay? Maybe for her it is. Maybe she has no incentive to get any better. After all, I have no problem understanding her. Even the deteriorated speech is good enough. She has a full and happy life. She goes to exercise class, has a boyfriend, a part-time job. Probably does much, much more; I'm not around to see it. Why change?

When is enough enough?

I'm one of those people who is rarely satisfied. I'm a little driven (some people would cough politely at this statement). I *want* to speak clearly. I *want* to walk smoothly. I *want* to use that right hand. I've learned to write with the left, but I wrote so beautifully with my right hand. I'd like to get that back.

I long for the days when progress came fast and easy. Every month, it seemed, I saw a big change. Boy, was I motivated! Getting completely well just seemed like a matter of time. There was actually a moment, during my second year, when I *felt* something snap into place in my brain, and suddenly my balance improved by quite a bit. Oh, to bring back those satisfying and easy changes!

Now everything feels like a battle. Seven years later I have learned a lot, but in some cases I have learned the wrong things, and the right ones seem further away than ever. And yet . . . when I try, really try, the improvement is immediate and so fast it is almost shocking.

There should be a program for people who have had strokes several years ago. But I find that very, very few people care about this; as long as you can function they feel their job is finished. But the job is not over. Not by a long shot. There is still plenty of room for improvement, it's just that very, very few people, professional or not, care anymore. They don't understand why you're still fighting.

I used to get lots of smiles and encouragement when I told people that I was working on improving. Now, not so much. I guess the people around me feel that I've come about as far as I can go. Why don't I stop?

It's understandable. For some people it *is* enough. For

me, it isn't. I know I can do better. It's just going to be very hard. Sweaty hard.

I think about the man, 89 years old, who stubbornly wanted to improve after a stroke. People like that often live to over 100, so why shouldn't his life be as good as it can be for those last eleven-plus years? *You go*, I wanted to tell him. Oh, he was strong and feisty.

So am I, and I'm nowhere near 89 years old. The way I see it, there's nothing wrong with taking a short break, but then you have to get back up on that horse called life and *keep working*. It will pay off some day. I'm convinced.

BLOGGING, JOURNALING, GETTING IT ALL DOWN

Once upon a time, (not so long ago in fact), I had a blog. Never mind the name. I did it out of boredom at work. We'd been bought out, the old company abandoned us, and the new one took several months to get around to my department. My workmates and I were all in a kind of purgatory.

As in *A Tale of Two Cities*, it was the best of times, it was the worst of times. We had nothing to do, which was great for about two weeks. Then the boredom set in. We got creative about it. There was a movie every day in the conference room, starting at 10:30 a.m. It was very well attended, I can tell you that.

There was a book exchange. If you read a great book, you gave a presentation about it (we were good at presentations), and you gave it to someone else who read it and passed it on, and so forth. We played games. Crossword abounded. Chess partners were plentiful; you had only to ask someone if they were interested. We had all kinds of office pools going; money was always changing hands.

Still, there were days when the hours dragged. *Is it time to go home yet?* It was on one of those days that I decided to start a blog.

With my boss's permission (blessing is more like it), I taught myself Wordpress. I started taking lots of pictures with my iPhone, because they were so easy to upload. I had a computer with a big screen, so my material looked great. And . . . my imagination was freed. I could blog about anything I wanted!

Soon I was spending two or three hours a day blogging. It took up my time; I had fun. There sure was nothing much else to do, and telling a writer to hang up her pen was like telling a horse to just stay in the stable. Uh-uh.

I had to scale it back when I started working again, but I continued to blog on evenings and weekends. The good news was that I had access to that big screen whenever I wanted, and I lived near enough to the office that it wasn't such a big deal to go in after hours. But I could also work at home on my own computer. It wasn't as pretty, but it sure was convenient.

Then I had a stroke. Unplanned, unwanted, incomprehensible. I lost my job. And I abruptly stopped blogging.

Now, I had gained a few followers, and they were plaintively asking me when I was going to start blogging again. Mind you, I had a hard enough time staying awake. After a couple of years, I could meet a friend for lunch, but that was it for the day. Afterward I would be completely exhausted. But my "fans" wanted me to pick up where I'd left off with my blog.

I didn't. The past few years I've concentrated on getting better. But when a friend mentioned my blog again one day, it set me to thinking. I might start blogging again.

After seven years, I can't imagine picking up where I left off. So much has changed! I felt like Rip Van Winkle after a year; imagine what seven years feels like. And now we're having a pandemic. Vaccines are a big help, but they're not 100%. It's hard to know what to do (or *not* do).

And my situation has changed so much! I've had a stroke; I was forced to retire; I've moved three times. This is a good test—am I ready for yet another change?

When you've had a stroke, you try so hard to recreate the life you used to have. It works partially. If you're lucky, you can go back to work or finish school. I was able to keep most of my friends, but some of them disappeared for various reasons. I couldn't quite keep up with the rest, at least not at first.

At some point, you'll realize your life needed some tweaking anyway, and now is a great time to do it. You might switch careers. Switch hobbies. Exercise a little differently. And yes, blog about different things.

Strokes are all about change. I changed on the outside, even though I didn't want to. But ultimately, want to or not, you need to change on the inside as well. You don't need to change your personality—no need to scare your family and friends. You've scared them enough.

The other thing is, you're going to forget. Right now, I can't remember very well what the first year felt like. If I blogged, or journaled, or just plain *wrote it down*, (which I actually did), I would remember certain things but not others. You think you'll never forget those terrible events, or the feelings you had, but you will over time. This may be a blessing for some, but for others it's quite distressing. When people ask me how long I was in the hospital, I'm chagrined to find that I can't answer them without looking at my notes. (It was five weeks, if you're interested.)

Writing, for some, is as painful as it gets. For others, it's cathartic. Writing about your stroke will ultimately help you, but only if it doesn't feel like another chore. We have enough of those to begin with.

THE
DIFFERENCES
BETWEEN
YEARS

L et's say, for discussion's sake, that it's been four years since my stroke. And I'm celebrating. I've come so far! I can now sign my name! I can put one foot in front of the other. Without a walker or a wheelchair or a cane.

Unfortunately, as I found, the people around won't be cheering so much. They saw me at my worst, when they were preparing for my death. Then they were relieved and delighted when I pulled through. Cheering me on, they saw me make a lot of progress in the first couple of years. Now, they're kind of . . . tired.

I really can't blame them. If I think I'm frustrated because progress now seems so slow, I can imagine how my family and friends feel. They don't want to celebrate, as I might, when I can reach overhead and put a frying pan back on its hook. *You* know what a big deal it is to reach your arm overhead and have enough control to know where the hook is and to meet it. They really don't.

I've found that the one question people very often ask is how many years it's been since I had my stroke. I now hesitate to tell them it's been seven years. Because when I say those words, *seven years*, the assumption is that wherever I'm at on the spectrum of recovery, that's it. It's all over. It isn't, but they've got recovery fatigue. Even *I* have recovery fatigue.

I miss the good old days when change came often and swiftly, like in the beginning. I was one of the lucky ones, in that usually that fast change only lasts one to two years. In my case, it lasted almost four years. Then change is slow, gradual, and hard-won. That's why it's so hard to stay motivated at this point. You just don't see the improvement, sometimes for a long time.

During the first year or two, as you're recovering fast, you're so enthusiastic. So is everyone around you. Because you're changing before their eyes, they're happy. You're happy. You think it will go on forever. It doesn't.

Some lucky people make full, or almost full, recoveries in that time frame. But many of them have a dirty little secret. You can backslide, or develop symptoms you never had before. This is so distressing you just don't want to tell anyone.

I know one woman who seemed to make a full recovery in two or three weeks. Now, a few years later, her balance is off and she sometimes slurs her words. These were things that she never did early on. Brain damage can happen slowly, over time, too.

Anyway, if you say you had a stroke, say, two years ago, people will *tsk tsk* and treat you like someone who's . . . recovering from a stroke. But if you say you had a stroke, say, ten years ago, it will seem like a lot of time has passed and, no matter where you are, you have fully recovered. If you're in a wheelchair, you'll always be in a wheelchair. Too bad.

I know a woman who got up out of her wheelchair and walked fourteen years after her stroke. It just took that long for her brain to recover. Now she walks with a cane, but I'll bet she surprised everyone. You can bet people asked her how long ago since she'd had her stroke, and she said, "fourteen years." They probably thought, *too bad*. They probably assumed all was over. Obviously, it wasn't.

At a certain point, and it doesn't take all that long, progress slows to the point where you think it's all over, too. Maybe you had your stroke... seven years ago! I have news for you. *I'm not done yet.*

Slow as it may be, I still make progress. And like my brother said, you'll know it by looking back.

For instance, I've just realized that I can now get into, and out of, the car like a normal person, one leg at a time. I used to have to swing both legs around and plant my feet firmly on the ground before I could stand up. Now I don't need to.

Could it be that all those exercises where I stood clutching the kitchen counter and balancing on one foot have finally paid off? Maybe they have. I *still* can't let go of the kitchen counter, but I can get in and out of my car more easily.

Will anyone rejoice over this? Well, no. But I will. This improvement came out of the blue, but it did come.

Early on, the changes are dramatic, and people's responses tend to be dramatic, too. After a few years, the changes are subtle and slow and not usually noticeable to anyone but you. It's so hard to stay motivated at this point. Yet if you don't, you won't keep improving.

Because . . . who knows what's around the corner? Today the car, tomorrow I may open my mouth and normal sounds may come out. Don't ever stop trying. You may surprise yourself when you least expect it.

PART
SIX

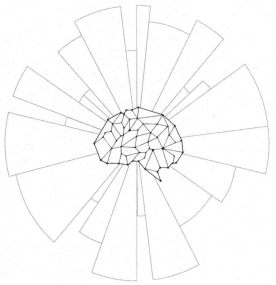

CAN YOU AFFORD TO GET BETTER?

We've all been there. "This can of tuna is so expensive! I can't afford it." Well, yes you can. You just don't want to spend that much on a can of tuna. It doesn't seem like good value for your money.

Stroke survivors are no different from anyone else on this matter. "I can't afford more therapy . . . a motorized wheelchair . . . that subscription to a service that helps you talk." So there are some difficult decisions to make.

Chances are, you can afford it. It just means giving up—temporarily—many of the things that make life sweet: Haircuts. Subscriptions to the sports channels. Magazines (which have become inexplicably expensive). A new computer or phone or some other electronic gadget.

Live without my mani-pedi? Unthinkable! I'll get depressed! It will defeat the whole purpose! Not really.

Therapy, while expensive, will not yield immediate results. You can't say, "Look how smooth my walking has become," the way you can say, "Do you like my new haircut?" It just isn't sexy to walk better. And after several months of practice, no less.

I can only say that a good therapist is worth his or her weight in gold and may change your life forever. I was fortunate enough to have a great physical therapist who was endlessly inventive. If one exercise didn't work, or I clearly wasn't that interested in it, he'd try another. Sometimes he came up with things that seemed downright undoable, but you know what? I did them.

Not only that, but six years later I'm still doing some of those exercises and repeating things to myself that he told me. I'm still, for instance, reminding myself that certain physical things I have to do often are just like the exercises I do all the time. *You can do this*, I tell myself, as I'm about to walk up a flight of stairs. It's just like what I do at the kitchen counter.

I'm not political, but I became political fast after I had my stroke. Because the state of California gave me the money I needed to hire therapists and caregivers for quite some time. Some people, who live in other states, don't get anything. You're supposed to put something aside for a rainy day instead. How many people actually do this? I'd be surprised if it's more than a handful.

People are always clucking about California being a high tax state. This included me! I would look at my paycheck stub and groan with disbelief about the money that was taken out. But guess what? When you have a stroke, which is about as rainy as it gets, suddenly the money is there. And did I ever need it!

In a perfect world, health care would be free and good. But this is not a perfect world. Far from it, in fact. Health care is expensive, not widely available, and spotty. For every Bret and Marilyn, terrific therapists who I will remember till my dying day, there are a dozen mediocre people who are just collecting a paycheck.

My insurance and California disability paid for most of what I needed. But guess who paid for that insurance? I groused about it, but it was there when I needed it. I didn't get mani-pedis. Maybe my nails weren't the best, but my insurance was paid up. And it's a good thing, because therapists cost a lot.

As with expensive shoes, there is a big difference between *I want* and *I need*—you might just have a case of the

"I wants." But when serious illness struck, I needed.

Nobody wants therapy. Yet as I found, it helped me do everything else I wanted to do. Like go to the beach (Ha! Got you there.) Walk fast for shelter when there is a sudden downpour. (There are few things more pathetic than the sight of a stroke survivor who is soaking wet. Because they couldn't run.)

No, it's not glamorous to read a few pages from a book and be corrected along the way by a speech therapist, who may suggest other things you can do to sound better. In fact, it's a drag.

But the woman who suggested I break words down into their components to pronounce them more properly? (Peet/sa for pizza, for example.) That's how I learned to pronounce multisyllabic words. That's why today I can say "specific" without fear.

Do you want to make progress? There are people who are trained to help if you want to make progress, but it does cost. Foregoing the subscription to ESPN, or that new pair of earrings, might be worth it.

THE
OTHER
SHOE

In this era where everybody's a hero and children get accolades for showing up at school, few people know what it's like to put your life on the line every minute of every day. Military people who have been deployed do, for sure. At this time of COVID-19, doctors, nurses, and other health professionals, certainly do. But so do people who have had strokes.

We live with the fact that we are at very high risk of having another stroke, one that we might not ever recover from. We could become vegetables. We could die.

How in the world can you deal with this? You can't, really, because it's a fact. Unlike other facts of life, if you ignore this one, it could have very bad consequences.

I find that I have to strike some kind of balance. You can't be like my gym teacher's mom, who at my last attendance at the gym had waited over twenty years to have another stroke. Because her doctor told her she would definitely have another one, probably within twenty years.

Twenty years! That's a long time to live with another stroke waiting in the wings. You could do a lot in twenty years. Have a whole career. Enjoy your retirement. Read a lot of books, listen to birdsong, watch good movies. Attend a lot of football games, play a lot of golf, catch a lot of fish. You get the idea.

This is hard to live with, but you don't really have a choice. In my case, different doctors have said different things. One neurologist said I would definitely have another stroke because my circulatory system had been "compromised," whatever that means (I can guess); another neurologist said I would never have another stroke because the one I had was so rare. It would be like getting hit by lightning twice. (Which happens.)

Who to believe? I prefer the second, but who knows; the first neurologist may have been right. Maybe my circulatory system has been compromised. Maybe it will rebel again someday.

I do know that whenever I don't feel well for whatever reason, the fear of another stroke comes galloping back. A few weeks ago, I fainted for two seconds or so. Long enough to wake up on the floor and know that I had truly blacked out. My mind immediately went to *I'm having another stroke*. In the shaky moments that followed, I went over my symptoms and found nothing to indicate another stroke. Everything pointed to me having done way too much. I was tired. So I went with that.

But I learned something important. Even though I rarely, if ever, think about having another stroke, my mind goes right there on the occasions when I don't feel well. And probably always will, if I'm to be honest. I don't think I can do anything about that. Maybe when twenty years have passed, I won't ever think about it. Maybe the medical researchers will find a cure.

If you've had a stroke, and if you think you'll have another one, that makes you ... a hero. A true hero, because, think about it or not, you face death every minute of every day. And somehow you deal with it.

This happens to others, too. I'll never forget the man at my rehab gym who, in recounting his story, said that during a routine checkup his doctor told him he had the heart of a 30-year-old (he was in his 50s). And he was so proud! The next day, though, he had a massive heart attack and actually died on the golf course. He was revived, and lived to tell the tale, because one of his golfing buddies was a doctor who administered CPR immediately and brought him back (it really can happen like in the movies).

That guy will live the rest of his life waiting for the next heart attack, even though he had surgery and they cleaned out his arteries. He's a hero, too.

Even stroke survivors at a higher risk might not have another stroke. Those who have had ischemic strokes probably brought their blood pressure down and check it carefully. Hemorrhagic stroke survivors like me have given up ibuprofen in favor of acetaminophen and stopped taking any medication that thins blood. I've been told that I'm a "bleeder," and I believe that because my father was, too. I probably inherited that tendency from him and will always have to watch it.

I don't think of myself as a hero. I don't pull pets out of burning buildings, rescue people who are stranded on their roofs because of flooding, or anything like that. Yet . . . I live with the knowledge that someday I may have another stroke. Judging from the people who have told me that they had a stroke ten, twelve, fifteen, twenty years ago, and whose faces change when they tell me, you never forget it. It's sobering.

I'm amused (well, *something* amuses me about this) to hear warnings about how you shouldn't do this or you shouldn't do that because *you might have a stroke*. Hello! I've already had one! And survived! And lead a somewhat normal life.

I think I'm a hero. And I don't forget it. Not for one moment.

NORMAL
VERSUS
LEADING
A NORMAL LIFE

I don't know about you, but my goal has been to be *normal*. A therapist (not a good one) told me, several years ago, that "normality is overrated"; she will be forever remembered for that remark.

By normal, I mean that *no one can tell I've had a stroke.* Until I tell them, which is at my discretion. This has been my goal. But now I'm beginning to wonder, do I really want that? Do I want to give up the privileges (yes, privileges!) that come with being somewhat disabled?

I would like to speak crisply and clearly, I know that. Yet my speech has greatly improved, and I don't even do all the exercises I should be doing. Shame on me, but reading out loud and repeating words gets boring, to say the least. But I've noticed that people are no longer afraid to call me on the phone, and it's rare that someone asks me to repeat something. I'm also not afraid to make phone calls and talk to strangers. This is very encouraging (and means I no longer have an excuse for making obligatory but annoying phone calls).

Since I mumbled to begin with, it's harder for me to enunciate, but I can do it, and I'm more understandable when I remember to do this. There isn't that one-second gap while people process what I say.

A while ago, along with millions of other Americans, I

saw Gabby Giffords speak to the nation. Brain damaged as she was, she spoke clearly, just as before! Now, that is my goal. And I know it is doable.

But Gabby Giffords let everyone know how hard it was for her to speak. Do I ever know about that! I find myself finishing sentences, out of breath and at the end of my rope, because I know that my listener expects it. I may be doing this for a long time, maybe forever.

That's where the reading out loud comes in. The voice is a muscle, and the more you use it, the easier it becomes to talk for a long time. That's how singers learn to sing. You need a good voice to begin with, of course, but there's a lot to learn, from breath control to stamina. Aphasia victims like me need to learn this.

Obviously, Gabby Giffords concentrated on this, because she is still paralyzed (or impaired) on one side. I noticed this because, at the podium, one arm just hung down, useless. I have a similar problem in that one side is out of control. People freak out a little when I drive them around, but in an emergency, when you need lightning-quick reflexes and superb control, my left side immediately takes over.

This is a lot of mumbo-jumbo to the average person, but it means a lot to a stroke survivor. However, it doesn't really answer the question, *are you normal or have you just learned to adapt?* And do you care?

Truth be told, I am slowly, slowly improving. I've been doing this blindly, not thinking about what it will mean to actually reach my goal. In the beginning, it pained me, for instance, to realize my beautiful handwriting was gone, as that hand is not capable of staying still long enough to write. Now I wonder, do I really want it back? What good did it do me? In this age of digital everything, who needs great handwriting, anyway?

That side is slowly getting better, but it may never be as good as it used to be. Do I care? I don't know.

But . . . being visible again, which is how I think of normality, comes with a price. You lose the handicapped placard for your car. You do everything at a normal pace, which is way too fast. Since you're no longer handicapped, you're no longer special in any way. You're expected to do…everything. Just thinking about that makes me tired.

In the beginning, I just wanted my old life back. But as time goes on, I start to wonder if that life was so great, after all.

I reached a point where I can do almost anything I used to do before. Maybe I do it differently, but I do it. I did say *almost.* I still miss those miles-long walks, long rambles on dirt trails or through city streets, exploring and finding some delightful things. There's a good goal: I want to be able to do that again.

But being somewhat handicapped means you have to rest more, stop earlier, not even try certain things. I'll never go to Machu Picchu. But maybe I can go to an outdoor art show and walk around.

Was I ready to give up certain things? I'd already done that by having a stroke. But was I now ready to give up those things that come with being handicapped? The answer is different for everyone, and you may surprise yourself. Maybe you need to get to a certain point and that's enough.

It's not lost on me that the people who recover fast, and completely, tend to be athletes. They are motivated and disciplined. They want to get back to normal in the worst way. They almost always succeed.

Recently I watched a movie about mountain climbers. One of them had a terrible accident and almost surely would never climb again. Almost. He fought his way back, learning to walk and talk again, building his strength until he could join his buddies on their next expedition. It was truly astounding, even to his friends. The kinds of things he did to recover were, to me, unspeakable. But recover he did. He went on to do something truly distinctive. Maybe that's the key.

I'm still contemplating just how far I want to go. I'm clear on some things, fuzzier on others.

You know those people who lose limbs and go on to

become triathletes? Outperform what most ordinary, *normal* people, people like you and me, could never do? Do you want to be one of those people?

For me, the jury's still out.

MY
SIGNATURE

My signature has changed. A lot. While I used to debate whether to put an extra flourish on the E, I'm lucky that I can make a capital E, flourish or no. This is because I can't use my right hand to write, and my left hand never learned that skill. It knows how to do it now. Badly, I think.

I'm better in the morning than in the late afternoon or evening, so I've learned to sign cards and fill out forms (some still need to be done by hand) in the morning. But I flinch when I go to a new doctor and have to fill out reams of paperwork first. When I am handed that clipboard and pen, my heart sinks. Delia, my caregiver, used to do this for me, but there hasn't been a Delia for many years now. I just have to do it on my own.

I am slow. My handwriting is spidery and sometimes illegible. I have to fill out my name, address, and phone number so often you'd think I'd be good at it by now. And sometimes I surprise myself and write well. But most of the time, I'm appalled at what I see.

I've signed contracts like this. Bought and sold a house. Signed tax returns. Got a new driver's license and registration for my car. No one has said anything yet.

The worst moment came when I had to sign the envelope that came with my voting ballot. Would I be questioned, or would my vote be thrown away? To my relief, no one said a word, and I've been signing with my left hand now for years, so it shouldn't be a problem. Ever. But you never know.

Interestingly, my new signature is slowly coming to resemble the old one. What does *that* mean? Am I so predictable? Maybe so!

I've never asked a lawyer if it's legal to sign with the wrong hand, but I figure it is. Look how many people break their wrists or hands and have to do this. Temporarily. The only difference is that I have to do it permanently.

If you've had a stroke, and your previously dominant side no longer works very well, you know about this. My admittedly biased advice is to sign away, because no one looks anyway. Or if they do, they figure rightly that for some reason you can no longer use that hand.

This is one of those everyday things that no one thinks about, like cutting a piece of chicken. You probably didn't think about it either, until you had to sign something. Then, whoops! You really have to do it, want to or not.

This is one of those rare times when you're better off adapting to the situation. Learning to use the previously good hand may take years. In the meantime, you have to sign a lot of things. During those years, or maybe forever, use the other hand. It may not be pretty, but it works.

THROUGH
THE
LOOKING
GLASS

One day, around my fourth year, I was staggering from the parking lot to the rehabilitation gym when I caught a glimpse of myself in the big glass double doors of the entrance. To my horror, I clearly dragged my right side behind me and looked very crooked. And walked scarily. Although I had come a long way, I had a flash of Breakfast with Idiots. I still looked bad. Much worse than I had thought.

A friend who's had a stroke said that someone she knew quite well had said something about her being severely disabled. "Do I really look that way?" she asked. I had to tell her that the answer was yes, she really did. I loved her just the way she was, but that was small comfort.

This is a problem for people who have what my friend calls "acquired disabilities." Like having a stroke later in life when you've been an avid outdoors lover—hiking, biking, fishing, rock climbing, etc. Or even indoors if you love to dance, play darts, play pool. It's bad enough that you can no longer do those things, but, if you're like me, looking in the mirror and seeing reality can be a horror show, too.

Almost all my life, mirrors have been my friends. Full-length mirrors were no big deal. They told me if my clothes looked fine, if my shoes matched my clothes. Did I need stockings or were my legs okay bare? Should I put a scarf on? Was I wearing too much jewelry, or not enough? The usual stuff.

Suddenly, after a stroke, you don't like what is staring back at you. Maybe you're in a wheelchair. Maybe, if you're a woman, you can no longer put makeup on, and you cut your long hair because you can no longer fuss with it. Or, like me, you're crooked and can't walk on one side.

The good news is, it's motivated me to learn to walk better on that right side, and to stand up straighter. Wheelchair users have an advantage in that they don't have to deal with this. But... wheelchair users have other problems. It all evens out in the end.

Early on, I avoided mirrors like the plague. I was gaunt. My head was half shaved. I had scars in the back of my head where the doctors had drilled into my skull. I hadn't yet learned to put eyeliner on with my left hand. I don't remember whether or not I could wear my contact lenses.

Jewish people put sheets over all the mirrors when a family member dies. That's how I felt. Cover those mirrors! I don't like them!

It is normal to dislike mirrors for a while. To be horrified by them, actually. To wonder how bad you look to others. Even if, like me, you care little about what others think. If you care a lot, it will be much harder.

Gradually, I learned to like mirrors again. I care, once again, if my shoes go with my clothes.

All of this takes a while. Years, maybe. In the meantime, some people avoid mirrors as much as possible, and ask themselves why their appearance means so much to them. I didn't care that much, but I was surprised to find out that I cared more than I thought. Meditate on that one for a little bit. In a society that values the color of your lip gloss more than it values what you think and feel, seeing a disabled person staring back at you in the looking glass can be uncomfortable.

Learn to love the way you are now.

THE
OTHER PERSON
SYNDROME

Now, I'm not a jealous person. Romantic jealousy when I was younger, yes. But I've never been jealous of people who had more, did more, seemed luckier than me. I just shrugged it off.

All that changes when you have a stroke. I thank my lucky stars that I wasn't envious to begin with, because all of a sudden you see everyday people doing everyday things you used to do. Making plans with another person, or a group of people, to eat at a restaurant, where they'll likely have to park a couple of blocks away and walk. (Yikes!) Riding their bicycles without a second thought. Laughing and saying "get *this*" to someone else, then reading whatever's funny, or unbelievable. When you can't even talk!

Sometimes it got the better of me. I just couldn't help it. I went home and licked my wounds. But . . . everyone has a sob story, and it helps—often a lot—to hear what these people are really going through.

In my old neighborhood, where I was living when I had my stroke, I used to see a woman riding her bicycle *uphill*, without huffing and puffing, every morning. She was not particularly muscular. I wondered how in the world she managed to do this. I was still dragging along with my walker, mind you. And, I'll admit, I was jealous. Even though I thought she must be out of her mind, because I wouldn't have tackled that hill *before* my stroke.

So one morning, instead of just waving hello, I flagged her down for a chat.

"Yes, this hill is something, isn't it?" she said cheerily. "But it takes my mind off other things. My husband has esophageal cancer, stage three, so it's touch and go for both of us. They removed his vocal chords, so he can't talk. He writes things down instead.

"My daughter does what she can, but she's got her own set of problems. Three kids and the father took off, who knows where. She can barely make ends meet. I'm her child care, because she can't afford anything else."

The woman went on and on, and by the time she was done, I was horrified and felt like hugging her. She had it so much worse than me!

But she said, "I see you struggling up this hill every morning, rain or shine, and it gives me such hope and courage. I think, 'If she can do it, I can do it!'"

I know another guy who appears fine, but I happen to have heard his sons are a mess (one is a drug addict, the other can't hold down a job for more than three months). They are always hitting him up for cash, and, out of guilt, he gives it to them. He was just diagnosed with Parkinson's. After losing his job.

I could say more, but you get the idea. Appearances can be very deceiving, and the people you are jealous of maybe would trade places with you in a heartbeat.

When you've had a stroke, your deficiencies are so *visible*. You look funny, you sound funny. People gaze at you and cluck sympathetically. But actually, they may be in much worse shape than you are.

A stroke gives you focus. You have just one goal in life: to get as well as you can. Or to function as well as you can. Everything else falls by the wayside. There is that one thing you can concentrate on.

Maybe you couldn't pay your bills before. Well, you've just had a stroke, so what about those bills? Maybe your spouse turned out to be a big disappointment and you didn't know what to do about it, but you've just had a stroke. Did someone say something about a husband or wife?

It's so easy to look at people who appear to be normal, and to be jealous of them. They must have it so great! Some people really do. Misfortune seems to have passed them by, those lucky devils. They seem to have it all—money, looks, great spouses, great children, overall success. Health! They are the ones who set your teeth on edge.

But you know what? They likely have their secret sorrows, too. And they can't have learned very much, since they may have gone to great schools, but they never attended the school of hard knocks. You learn more there than at Harvard.

I'm just like everyone else. Sometimes I look at "normal" people and I wonder "Why me? Why did I have a stroke and they didn't?" I'll never have an answer to that one. Repeat, *I'll never have an answer.* I finally have figured my stroke out technically, but that doesn't answer the greater question. I'll just never know why my body didn't handle my stroke very well.

In the meantime . . . this is what I've been given to work with, like it or not. It's like having blue eyes, or curly hair. It just is.

Envy is inescapable but often misplaced. Is the person you envy really enjoying their life more than you are? If the answer is yes, *that's* the thing you need to change. Your life, not your stroke.

It's so easy to use the stroke as an excuse. You might decide to never exercise because you've had a stroke. You might eat whatever you want, because you've had a stroke and don't want to deprive yourself of anything. Career? Well, that's over. You've had a stroke!

There are things a stroke survivor probably never will do again, but the stroke can't prevent you from having a full life. You can still help your kids, or grandkids, with their homework. It may take some creativity, but you can still have a career. Friends. A social life.

I look at those people I envy and realize they don't have it any better than me. *Different*, maybe, but not better. And then I go do the dishes. Because I can.

STROKES
AND
DRINKING

'm not a heavy drinker. I can go weeks without having a drink and never notice it (except that my wine cellar will turn to vinegar soon). My doctors have all said, "Don't drink." I'm a bleeder, and drinking thins my blood, which is exactly what I don't need. Yet, I wonder... if my neurologist said my stroke is very rare indeed and I'll never have another, why can't I drink in moderation?

If you've had an ischemic stroke and your doctor says it's okay, you're in a much better position to drink. Your blood could use some thinning. But if, like me, you've had a hemorrhagic stroke, you have to be more careful. I drink occasionally, but not like before.

People are funny about this. They look upon it as an aberration, when all you're really trying to do is protect yourself. When you put it that way, they are much more comfortable. But you may not be!

I doubt whether alcohol, taken in moderation, has sent anybody to the emergency room. But there is one good reason to not drink, or stay home when you do. That is, having a glass of wine or a cocktail, or two, affects your balance. I don't know about you, but anything that makes me dizzy is something to stay away from. I'm balanced precariously enough as it is. I don't even like it when it gets windy out! You have to lean into the wind a bit to stay upright. I have enough trouble staying upright!

That said, when everybody is chatting and holding a glass of (good) wine in their hand, I want one, too. Everything else be damned. So I have that one luscious drink, and then I stop. I still have to walk to the other room later. I'll do it, but I do have to pay for that one glass of wine. It's worth it!

You know those movies where the hero or heroine drinks too much and has to be helped up the stairs, then put to bed like a little kid? I used to laugh over those scenes. It's not funny any more. It's kind of horrifying.

I wish I could be lighthearted about drinking, but when you're afraid of falling, getting tipsy is not a good idea. If you've made a full recovery and feel completely normal, be my guest. But if you even have a little residue of stroke, watch it. One glass will do. Anything more and you may be courting disaster.

ADVERTISING
AND STRESS
IN GENERAL

Everyone says "Don't get stressed." Or, "Stop and smell the roses." Take time off. Get a life.

Stress is considered such a bad thing. But here's what it isn't—a light switch that you can turn on and off. Presto change-o—look at me, I'm not stressed! This hike in the woods did the trick!

Oh, I wish it were true. Wouldn't it be easy.

Once I took a design class at UC Berkeley and the teacher said, "The number one stressful career in the United States is—drumroll—advertising!" My chosen profession! Did that make me feel good (no). But a profession where you are at the mercy of other people (your boss, your clients), under ridiculous deadline pressure (you want it *when?*) and where you have to be creative every single day whether you feel like it or not, is pretty stressful. Well, very stressful. In fact, you don't even realize how stressful it is.

I remember when I was in my 30s, and the stress had already built up in my body, thinking, *I'm going to pay a high price for this someday.* Well, someday came. I had a stroke. Stress is not the only reason, but still. When you remove the factors, and high stress is one of them, maybe I wouldn't have had a stroke. Is that true for you, too?

This is a tough one. I was single (after one marriage and a couple of relationships, one of which was very long term), owned a home, owned a dog, had lots of friends and a busy social life. Pretty normal, you think. But maybe not so normal.

I once visited a friend at her country home (she took her laptop and worked most of the weekend), and when we finally "relaxed" before dinner with a glass of wine, I could see her balling her hands into fists. Ready to fight invisible enemies. Was this relaxing? I don't think so.

I had a boss with a skin condition and an alcohol problem (a polite way of saying he was a drunk). Various friends and coworkers had weight problems, although we lived in California, land of the slim and exercise-obsessed. One woman, at a young age (early 30s) was a mess of health problems. A youngish guy, a proofreader, quit. I could go on and on, but you get the picture.

We live in a stressful society. In fact, it's something of a badge of honor to say, "I'm so stressed out." But all that stress can, and often does, contribute to a stroke.

It used to be stressful to keep everybody fed and clothed. For a lot of people, it still is. But those not in that category are probably victims of what I think of as manufactured stress. You have what you need, but you want more. In some cases, a lot more. And you're willing to risk health problems to get it.

My therapist Bret told me he saw more and more strokes at younger and younger ages. I don't know about you, but every time I say I've had a stroke, the listener knows at least one other person who's had one. That's a lot of people! Some thrive on this kind of pressure, but others do not, yet they are subject to such peer pressure, not to mention internal pressure, that they end up leading an unnatural life. And they have strokes.

Packing up and moving to Bali to become a beach bum isn't an option for most of us. Yet having a stroke, possibly with damage that will stay with you your whole life, makes you think. Maybe you weren't cut out for a high-stress life to begin with.

I remember, way back in the mists of time, earning my

college tuition by doing menial office work. I remember thinking, *this isn't so bad*. Probably, if I had stayed in that job, in five years I would have started chafing, but it made me think. By getting a college degree, was I fulfilling my own expectations or those of other people?

Having a stroke makes you reevaluate your whole life. And gives you a good reason to do less, and enjoy doing less. Maybe, if we all lived that way, strokes would be much more rare than they are now.

More
Motivation

A guy without legs learning to walk is great motivation, but that motivation wears off after a while. In fact, after a couple of years, you don't remember all that much. So I had a second motivating factor, right in my old neighborhood.

Another guy—we'll call him Jay—was perfectly normal and one of the nicest men you could ever meet. I would see him often out walking with his wife and stop to chat with them. This was BEFORE my stroke.

One day, while on his way to work in the morning, Jay had an "episode" at the coffee shop. There was a frantic phone call (there always is), and Jay and his wife ended up at the hospital. He was mostly paralyzed.

To this day, doctors don't know what happened to Jay, which is kind of frightening, but he was in that hospital for weeks. Even after he came home, he was bedridden for months. No one knows what kind of shape he was in, but he had a terrific spouse, who took really good care of him.

To say Jay was never the same is an understatement. It took him many years to learn to walk again. For most of that time, he used a cane. I used to see his uncoordinated self out walking, gamely, and would wave hello or stop to talk. He got better and better, until, when I left, he looked good.

But ten years had passed. That was how long it took him to almost fully recover.

In the meantime, I had a stroke. Jay's mysterious illness took on new meaning for me. I began using him as a role model. He never gave up. He learned to walk again! And, even better, I found out through chatting with him on the street that he had started going to concerts and lectures with his wife. He traveled all over the world, walked around in strange cities.

If there's one thing I've learned, it's that anything can happen to you at any time. It can happen even to those who think their life is perfect just as it is. I'm sure Jay thought that nothing would ever happen to him. But it did.

Here's a good motivation: someone who had a great life also had a life-changing event and came back valiantly. It took him many, many years to do it. He went gray during the process (probably would have anyway, but who knows?), never worked again, probably never again did a number of things, but he ended up with a good life, just different from what he had planned.

So this was my goal: you will have a new life, but a different one. I'm sure if you asked Jay, he would probably choose to not go through what he did, but he dealt with it. Beautifully, if you ask me.

EXERCISING

One of the hardest things for me to do is sit still. I'm a go, go, go type of person. This does not pair well with having a stroke. It's been one of the hardest things for me to adapt to—stopping when I've had enough.

For the first year, I didn't want to do anything but sleep. I could drop off into slumber land at any time of the day or night. Like a cat.

The rare times I was up for three or so hours, I was so dizzy that I was afraid to move. That took care of a lot of things. I went from the bed to the couch and back again. My caregiver didn't have to scold me, because truthfully, I hardly ever moved.

Gradually, my energy began to come back, and I do mean gradually. I'm in my eighth year now, and it wasn't till year six to seven that I finally gave up my afternoon nap and stayed up throughout the day and evening like a normal person.

Having a stroke must do an incredible number on your body, because it takes years to get your energy back. You won't even realize it's happening until one day you run around doing things, never sleep, and it's okay. But until then, what a ride!

I must have missed my old routine, because I started exercising in my second year of recovery. I stayed low on the floor because I didn't have any balance yet. My caregiver hovered over me nervously, but she did give me pointers, too. "Lift that leg higher!" And, "Keep that arm steady!"

She was a good personal trainer.

Soon I regretfully had to say good-bye to that caregiver, Delia, whom I truly loved but could not afford anymore. Has anyone noticed that the cost of care has skyrocketed and so have insurance premiums, but your policy runs out just as it would have twenty years ago? I'm just saying. The hidden cost of healthcare, as if it's not expensive enough, is that it runs out fast, and then you're not covered any longer unless you have a new incident. Which nobody wants.

I was now exercising at home most days, but around year three, I started going to a rehabilitation gym. This was no ordinary gym. It was in a hospital, for one thing. Apparently, there are few of them in the United States, although I don't know why. Most of the people in that gym were recovering from heart attacks or strokes, or were disabled in some way. It was a terrific gym, and I still miss it.

Everyone was jovial. You heard a lot of jokes. Dying and coming back was nothing unusual to this crowd. I had nicknames for some people, including Rock Out Lady, who got on the treadmill, put in her ear buds, and danced to music no one else could hear. You should have seen her face! It was ecstatic, and this woman had had a stroke and walked with a cane. It took her ten years to get out of a wheelchair and walk.

I loved Rock Out Lady and looked forward to her coming to the gym. But I also got introduced to the machines. My goal was to use the stair stepper, but I never stopped shaking enough to do it. I did use the rower, the stationery bicycle, and some sort of device that strengthened biceps and triceps. Making it to the water cooler was still problematic, and I think everyone held their breath until I was safely there, but overall it was a homey little crowd, presided over by two RNs who specialized in rehab and watched everyone like a hawk.

Then came the sorry moment when one of the rehab RNs gently told me I was ready to go to a regular gym. The rehab gym was one place I didn't want to graduate from, but I didn't stay much longer.

I moved to the Central Coast of California (more about that in another section) and didn't exercise for a while. My house had three stories so I walked a lot of stairs, and it took me a few months to unpack. But then I signed up for two classes: Balance and Flexibility, and Gentle Yoga, which turned out to be not so gentle.

When I started the Balance and Flexibility class, I needed my cane just to walk to the barre. I hung on there for dear life, and was only able to do about half the exercises. A few months later, I could do just about everything and could walk to the barre without my cane. I could also sit on the big balance ball without falling off. *And* do the exercises.

The one thing I had trouble with was getting from my car to the exercise room. The classes were held in what looked like a WWII-era barracks, and the sidewalk, if you could call it that, was cracked, broken, and uneven. I needed a flat and smooth surface. Clearly they didn't expect people like me in there.

Gentle Yoga was in a room right next to Balance and Flexibility class, but was held on different days. That class was harder. I had a yoga mat, but I kept falling over, anyway. I pity my neighboring yoga aficionados, who gasped a lot and tried to help. I was careful not to fall from a standing height because I didn't want to break any more bones. This meant not doing most of the standing exercises.

In a few months, I could do almost all the poses, including the standing ones. I mastered downward dog again. I could do warrior pose without the barre on my good side.

Why am I telling you all this? Because I was willing to look bad at first, and look how much I learned. We can't expect to spring from the ocean all glowing and perfect. Maybe Botticelli would appreciate it, but it doesn't happen that way to people who have had strokes.

I moved again, this time to Florida. After a few months, I joined a Pilates studio. There are a couple of yoga poses, but everything else is new. And fast.

Now, speed is my enemy. I do everything slowly and carefully. But it has dawned on me that the world moves faster than I do and if I want to keep up at all, I'd better learn to move at a quicker pace.

I'm now on about my seventh Pilates class, and already I can move a little faster, do a little more. The teachers of these classes are so wonderful. They really appreciate the effort you put into it, and they are your best cheerleaders when you learn to do something you couldn't do before. They are there not only to guide the class, but to help you be the best that you can be.

In a few months, I expect to get through a Barre class without thought or worry. Who knows what's next?

BEING DISABLED
IN A
LESS THAN
PERFECT WORLD

I noticed something a few months ago. People would ask when I had my stroke, and if I said three years or so, I would be assured that there was lots of improvement ahead of me. At five years or so, it became more problematic. I would still be assured of improvement, but with less enthusiasm. Now, at seven years, I've reached the point where I'm afraid to tell the truth. Because I've found that sympathy has an expiration date, and at some point people just assume that you've gone about as far as you can, and you're obviously disabled for life. Although you know differently.

What do you do about this label?

I've tried telling people, in a rush, that I'm still improving. "Seven years but I'm getting better all the time." Something like that.

It goes over like a lead balloon.

You can hear them thinking, *Seven years? Well, she's done. Clearly doesn't want to admit it. I'll play along.*

Those same people will be astonished, and impressed, when they see you in six months, and you've made progress. And then—again—they'll think you're done.

I'm training myself to walk without a cane. I pretty much can get through a whole dog walk now this way. If it's raining, so much the better. I can't put up an umbrella, use a cane and carry a leash all at the same time. So I ditch the cane and put the umbrella on my shoulder instead. No cane! So far, I haven't fallen.

This is a big deal to me, but not to others who see me out walking with my dog regularly. You have to get used to this. Therapists will notice every little thing, and crow about any progress you make, but to a normal person you're just getting more normal. It's about time, too.

Although being disabled has its uses, it makes you a pain in the neck, too. You walk too slowly, get out of the car too carefully, maybe can't go long distances. I remember a friend telling me that the restaurant she was taking me to was *right there*. It turned out to be three blocks away, and I had to walk those three blocks at night, over tree roots and other things you can trip over. She didn't think anything of it. I was shaking in my boots. (I did it, however.)

You know what it was like to take your 90-year-old aunt somewhere? You did it uncomplainingly, out of love, but that was just a few hours out of your day. Imagine doing it all the time. Or almost. That would be hard to take, for anyone. No matter how much they love you or how devoted they are. You're still cramping their style.

You can get around this by only surrounding yourself with other disabled people, who also move slowly and are limited in what they can do. They'll cheer you on, for sure. But they don't want you to be normal, or close to it, because then you'll possibly want to leave them. It's a conundrum, which I'll tackle in another chapter.

I have also found that attitudes vary by state and even possibly by county, as many laws do. To my surprise, I found that Californians are very empathetic, helpful, friendly. Floridians, on the other hand, often find you just a nuisance. That is not to discount the many wonderful people I've met here. There's just a difference, and I've noticed it.

At some point, the stroke survivor needs to decide whether or not to permanently join the ranks of the disabled, or whether it's more important to "pass," for lack of a better word, as normal, and have this be the goal. I will tell you that the only people who like the disabled are other people with disabilities, and their therapists and caretakers. Once you join that world, it is very hard to get out. I'm just saying.

I think the best of all worlds would be to be friends with everybody, including the disabled and folks who appear to be "normal." (You often find out otherwise). That way, you can always have your finger on the pulse and not identify with anyone but yourself. We're all different, right? This is a chance to prove it.

Self-Love

This may sound cheesy, but do you love yourself? Warts and all?

It's easier to say "yes" when those warts are relatively small—like big feet or difficult hair. Maybe you think you're too short or too tall. These are things you can learn, over time, to get past. That's part of the wisdom that comes with age. You learn to accept, no *love*, yourself just the way you are.

What was all the fuss about when I was 25? Why did I spend, I mean waste, all those hours in front of the mirror fretting about things that turned out to be so petty? Having better hair or a smaller chin won't change your life. Confidence, that most sexy of assets, will.

Now, how are you supposed to be confident, to love yourself, if you can't walk or talk? Those are big flaws. You can't simply flash a big smile when you're in a wheelchair. If the people around you notice you at all, they don't pay you much attention. Unless they are therapists or have some big, important flaw of their own, the stroke survivor is at the bottom of the heap.

Unless—and this is not easy—you are persistent and insistent and let your personality shine through. I may not be able to walk, for example, but I can think. I can read, I have opinions. I can tell jokes, clown around. Drink beer or wine, be a great companion. Make everyone sit up and take notice.

Some people, who can't believe how far I've come, have called me a "miracle." (From being pretty much a vegetable.) But I'm no miracle. I'm someone who simply refused to give up who I am. I did not shrink into the woodwork. I'll say that again, loud and clear. *I did not shrink into the woodwork.*

Do I love myself, though? That's a hard question to answer. I guess, if pressed to do so, I'd have to say I like myself quite a bit. I don't feel sorry for the people who come around, just as I'm sure they don't feel sorry for me. Being with others is a pleasure. I know we'll do it again soon because *we had such a good time.*

It's so simple, yet so difficult. If you feel sorry for yourself, others will feel sorry for you. If you're visibly struggling, they'll help you gladly, but they'll associate you with hard times. If you dwell on your stroke, so will they.

If you let the stroke define your life, well, for the rest of your life, you'll be the person who had the misfortune to have had a stroke.

You had a stroke, and you'll never be the same. But you will still be you. Instead of going to an office, you're doing something else. I lost my job, but I've found new purpose as a writer. Because that is my talent. I can't sing, but I sure can write.

Self-love is hard to achieve even if you don't have a life-changing event like a stroke. But if you stop dwelling on what you've lost and instead think about what you've gained (and stroke survivors have gained a lot), it is possible. It is possible to love yourself even if you're bedridden, if you're in a wheelchair, if you walk and talk funny.

They say laugh and the whole world laughs with you. The same is true about self-love. And self-acceptance. Achieve them, and the whole world will love and accept you. You can't ask for more than that.

MY
BOOK CLUB

When I lived on the Central Coast of California, I joined the local library book club. I could tell the other members were surprised that I had the gumption to do this, as I came in with my cane, had to help move chairs around, couldn't talk well. (*Ss* and *Rs* were still a problem.)

Once seated, I was fine. The moderator, a woman named Sally, ended up having everyone sit in a big circle and went around the group, giving everyone about five minutes to speak. The group was that big. I ended up not liking this at all, as it reminded me too much of a classroom. Eventually, I dropped out, but this was back when I was still in the group.

I was accepted, no problem (at least I think it was no problem; maybe people talked about me after the group). This happy state of affairs went on for a few months.

Then, somehow, word got out to the community that there was a disabled woman in the group. And the group started to change.

It started with one guy in a wheelchair who came in with his caretaker. They listened to the book on tape, because he couldn't read, and both fit right into the group. Both gave their opinions. It was great.

And then it snowballed. A blind guy joined the group,

then a woman who didn't quite have her emotions under control, and she dominated the group at one meeting for a half hour because she never stopped talking (and crying). The members were so polite about this, but I remember thinking, *she doesn't belong here.* She just wasn't normal enough to fit into the group.

When I left, there were six disabled people in the group, which had increased in size so much that we all had maybe two minutes to speak. You can't say much in two minutes. You can't do much in two minutes. This is how I came to understand that there are degrees of disability. I had been discounting all those friends and relatives who referred to me as slightly disabled. The people who joined the group were *profoundly* disabled.

It must be so confining to be in a wheelchair, have an illness or handicap that won't ever improve, need a caregiver. But where do you draw the line about joining a group?

I know people in wheelchairs who would be most welcome in any group. They are sharp, opinionated, have no trouble talking, have something to contribute. A couple of the people who joined my book club fall into this category, and they were most welcome. But some of the people who joined were not capable of keeping up. I think this is a good criterion.

The measure should be: Can you follow what's going on? Keep your disruption to a minimum? Follow the rules, whether you agree with them or not? Then you'd be a *great* book club member.

Caregivers are generally thrilled to have an outing, and they read the books and give their impressions and opinions, too. This is all pretty marvelous. But if it's too hard, have the courage to tell your caretaker, too. There's probably another group you can fit right into. Or... start one of your own! You'll be surrounded by grateful people.

Do You Really Need One of Those Call Things?

We've all seen the ads. They strike fear in your heart, as they are meant to do. Help! I've fallen down and I can't get up! Well, just press the call button you wear around your neck, and help will come fast. It's that simple—or is it?

I've thought long and hard about those call buttons. For a monthly fee, you can buy peace of mind. I still don't have one, which should tell you something. Maybe I'm foolish. But nothing, and I mean nothing, in life is so simple.

Maybe it's because I was in advertising. It sure teaches you not to trust any corporation, because basically they are moneymaking machines. As a copywriter, I was trained to lie. Not *lie* exactly, but put things in a certain light that would lead to the wrong conclusion. Cherry-pick the truth.

I could make anybody believe anything. Congrats to me for being such a great manipulator, but it's very hard to fool me now. I know about the big motivators—fear, sex, money, power—and none of them are good. Altruism is not one of them.

Take that ad for a call button. On the surface, it seems to be nothing but good. If you've fallen and can't get up, you might really need one. But . . . what if you're unconscious by then? The paramedics will have to break your door down. Unless you prearrange the whole thing, they will take you to the nearest hospital for treatment, maybe not the one you want to go to. Who will take care of your house, your dog? No call button is going to get your life in order.

Meanwhile, a lot of things will be private and out of network, so your medical insurance may not pay for it. Leaving you with a huge bill that it will take you years to pay off and that may affect your quality of life forever. All for a small monthly fee.

You see where I am going with this?

Now, if you live alone or spend a lot of time by yourself, it may be a good thing for you. Some people have a round robin of phone calls at a certain prearranged time that I frankly think is a much better idea. Keys are shared so your friends and family can get into your house. You want people who are smart and experienced and know you well to call an ambulance, choose a hospital, or choose a doctor. All of which you may or may not be able to do.

I was by myself when my stroke happened. Luckily, I remembered a friend's cell phone number, luckily she answered. Luckily, she lived up the street and had my key. She was a reluctant emergency contact, but she was smart and quick and knew what to do. I was lucky, lucky. But . . . a call button wouldn't have helped me the way she did.

Recently I saw a full-page ad for free cell phone apps that do the same thing. I'll get one of those, because why not? I'll probably have to enter a whole bunch of things, like my emergency contact and what hospital I would like to go to. Just thinking about it gives me the willies.

But I believe in that saying, *hope for the best, but prepare for the worst.* So I'm hoping I never have another stroke. But just in case I do, or some other thing happens, I'll be prepared.

Bad fortune can strike anyone, at any time and in any place. But for stroke victims, it already has. That makes us different. *Does it make us better?* I hope it does.

PART
SEVEN

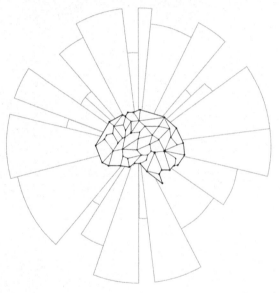

MOVING
TIME

Some people may never have this problem. But I'm a restless soul, and I've moved three times since having my stroke. The first move was several hundred miles away, from Northern California to the Central Coast of California (*Sound of Music* country; it's so beautiful you could burst into song). That was hard enough, but the second move was across the whole country to Florida. I should have my head examined (ha!) for this, but I did half the packing for both moves myself. With help from friends. And the second time, I had to take two airplane flights and put my dog in cargo. The airline employees took good care of her, but I was a mess. *Never again*, I vowed. Then I moved again.

Here's the thing: life doesn't stop because you had a stroke. The birds still sing, the ducks still quack, you still need to walk the dog. And possibly (in my case, definitely) move.

Besides the usual problems, you could be faced with a bigger quandary: how am I going to get from here to there when I can't walk very well? How am I going to pack up all my stuff when only one hand works? There's nothing like trying to use a tape dispenser with one hand. It's hard enough with two.

It's clear that the world is not going to come to your aid all the time. In some cases, none of the time. So I mostly had to face that sea of boxes by myself. I had help with my moves from wonderful friends, but there were still days when I had to do things without them. I could have crawled into bed and thrown the covers over my head, but I didn't.

How did I manage? The same way you take a ten-thousand-mile journey: you start with a single step. In this case, a single box.

I lost track of how many times I had to throw away tangled-up tape. Tape can be evil; it has a mind of its own and twists when you least expect it to. Like when you are just closing up a box. This is a test of nerves and your language (can you keep it clean?).

So in addition to moving being one of the most stressful things you can do, you have the added stress of packing up when your body doesn't work the way it should. Figuring out how to get from Point A to Point B. No wonder I don't want to ever move again. Even though I probably will.

You know what helped? I kept repeating the words my favorite therapist told me. "Do what is hard; then what is easy will be *really* easy. Moving is hard! Everyday life seems like a breeze in comparison!

Maybe some are lucky, and can just stay where they are and vegetate in place. But if you have to move, know that it's possible. Not easy, but possible. You'll have to get used to a new place with a new configuration. This is where you learn how much you're used to that step down onto the porch or that loose floorboard on the stairs. My first move was to a three-story townhouse, and was I ever sorry. All those stairs! I got used to them, but in spite of the fact that they keep your legs in good shape, I was happy to leave. I'll never do THAT again.

After the second move, my new home is all on one level, which is a relief. But there is a big step down to the back porch, which I'm all too aware of. In the beginning, I was terrified of that step. Now I just accept it as part of my house. I hold onto the sliding glass doors (heavy, thank goodness), and take a step down.

I don't want to even think about what I'd do if the doors weren't there. I've become an expert at looking around me to see what there is to hold onto. Usually there's *something*. My nightmare is a big, open space where I have to step up or down, or get up or down, without holding onto anything. (I'm working on this.)

Getting back to moving—I was amazed at how adaptable I am. Having a stroke doesn't change that. It may take me a little longer to learn something new, but learn I do. By hook or crook.

Packing up and moving is a big test for anyone, but it's a bigger test for those who are handicapped. But you know what? It's a test we can pass with flying colors. Don't let fear stop you. Ever.

THOSE THINGS
THAT
HAUNT YOU

I've been battling aphasia and ataxia for years. Although I hope not, I may be battling them for life. This is why people think "yeah, yeah" when I say I'm improving. I can now pronounce *Ss* and *Rs*, but all they hear is a thick, tight voice. I'm walking more smoothly, but all they see is a woman who walks more slowly than them, using a cane when it's difficult. Big sigh.

This isn't stopping me. I *am* getting better, even if no one else notices it. They only notice the big things. Like, now, I carry my cane most of the time. *That* gets noticed, and I have to say, I'm proud of it. I'm getting a much better handle on what I need to do to walk better. As I've said before, walking has so many components it can make your head spin. And *everything* is connected, so if your hips aren't working right, your walking will be off, too.

Add to that mix a mild amount of ataxia, and you've got a real problem. Not insurmountable, but a problem. Ataxia is defined (by the Mayo Clinic) as a loss of control and coordination, potentially affecting your speech, your gait, swallowing, your thyroid function, and tremors. To that I would add that my right side feels "lighter" than my left, which makes pretzel poses easier on that side, but makes everything else more difficult.

If your cerebellum and/or spinal cord have been injured

by stroke, you are left with ataxia. Guess where I had my stroke? On my cerebellum. And I felt the blood go down my spinal cord, so I wouldn't be surprised if that was affected, too. One moment can wipe out everything you learned to do as a child. It's sobering.

When I try something requiring small motor skills, my hand (or foot) starts to shake wildly, as if to say, "No! Don't make me do that!" So I can use my right hand to, say, lift a big box, but not to write my name.

This is terrifying sometimes, as I can't depend on that hand or foot to intervene and save me if I lose it. I know this, because it's happened. Luckily, my left side, which is back to normal, can do this, but it's not like being left-handed, where your right can take over if need be. I am in deep trouble if my right side has to take over, because it can't. It flails wildly. It's not pretty to look at.

And it's *useless* at useful things, like grabbing something when I'm falling. If my left side doesn't take over, I'm toast.

It's a little bit like having one kidney, or one eye. You learn to be extra-careful about the remaining one, because really, that's the only one.

The list of things that can cause ataxia is as mind-boggling as the condition itself, but stroke is one of them. So is severe COVID-19. So those poor souls, if they survive, may be triumphant temporarily, but then ataxia can rear its ugly head.

Here's what *I* think. The brain is a marvelous organ, and in many, many cases can repair itself or build new circuits alongside the old ones. So if you've had a stroke and are left with ataxia, you need to build new circuits to take over from the ones that are damaged. I don't see why ataxia should be any different from anything else. In fact, CI (constraint-induced) therapy has been quite successful in restoring the side that doesn't work so well. The only (ha!) trouble with CI therapy, which has you wear a cast on the good arm and only use the bad one, is that you need someone who's willing to be there *all the time* to help you eat, dress, turn the pages of a book, etc., until you can do it yourself. This could take months.

The horrible part is, I had gotten over my ataxia almost completely, and then I broke my hip. By the time I started walking again, my ataxia had come roaring back, and I haven't beaten it after two or so years. No doubt there's a medical reason for this, but for me it's enough to make me gnash my teeth.

Then we have aphasia.

Aphasia, like ataxia, can take many forms. Basically, it's when your speech is affected. Some people can't talk at all. Others lose certain vowels or consonants. Your brain draws a big blank when you have to pronounce them (like me losing my *Ss* and *Rs*). Some people can only whisper or can only sing. Some cannot understand what is being said to them, because the connection between words and meaning has been so damaged. Others can understand everything and can speak, but their speech is slow and halting. Others, like the actress Sharon Stone (who beat it, good for her!) are left with a stutter.

I suppose I'm lucky. My frontal lobe was not affected, so I have no problem reading or understanding anything. Other people do, very much so. This also can be overcome with a lot of work and patience.

For the first couple of years or so, I spoke only gibberish. Talk about frustration! My mind worked fine, as fast as ever, but I couldn't speak very well. I became a very, very good listener. I also learned to be succinct. This gave people less to try to figure out. I learned quickly, when people answered a question I hadn't asked, or mumbled "Yes," that they hadn't understood me. I became a master at saying things a different way. It does not help to say the same thing over and over again, until both you and your listener feel foolish and helpless. Make them, and yourself, feel better about the whole thing by learning to say so something differently on a dime.

I'm quite understandable now. However, my voice, as a

friend described it, is very tight, and talking takes a great effort for me. It seems like I run out of breath with every word. But it took me seven years to get here, and I'm far from perfect. I still sound like Donald Duck.

Here's where the medical profession falls down on the job. The speech therapist I was assigned was clearly right out of college and often had her textbook open on her lap. All she did was have me read easy books out loud. She could barely hide her boredom and often yawned in my face.

This was serious business for me. Still is. So, I'm begging—please don't become a therapist if it's just a job and a paycheck for you. Don't do it unless you are dead serious, because the person sitting in front of you certainly is. They really want to talk. They expect you to have a bag of tricks from which you can pull the one thing that will help them. It *does not* help to have a therapist who can't do anything, or doesn't care enough to.

I've had a lot of time wasted by therapists. I've been told this, too, by others who have had strokes. By trial and error, and by feedback from friends, I discovered what worked and what didn't. I shouldn't have had to do this. Stroke patients shouldn't have to do this. But that's reality.

The laws have to change. Therapy has to change. Insurance has to change. In many cases, therapists are doing the same things they did seventy years ago. This is unacceptable. You wouldn't go hunting with a bow and arrow, would you? Yet this is the equivalent of what most therapists do.

So yes, I still have aphasia. I'm still improving. I expect that two years from now, I won't sound like this anymore. Who knows what I'll sound like?

The point is to *never give up*, no matter what you've been told. Sometimes the most well meaning medical people are dead wrong. You know what you're capable of. Show them.

HOME
ALONE

t started when I came home from the rehab hospital. My east coast brother, who had been staying at my house, had a plane back home to catch. So he had to run out the door. "The caregiver will arrive at any moment," he told me. And then the door closed. And I was alone.

I had never had a problem being home alone; in fact, I rather liked it. But this time I could barely walk, needed a walker, talked gibberish, couldn't get down the two steps to the living room. I was so dizzy I barely knew which way was up. And I was home alone.

I had a little breakfast room off the kitchen, I went there to wait *because I couldn't get anywhere else*. I picked up a book and waited.

It took about two hours for the caregiver to arrive. Now, two hours weren't very much, and normally they would go by as fast as the blink of an eye. But when you can't do anything, two hours is a long time. It feels like two days. I was afraid to leave the breakfast room, afraid I would be found in a heap on the floor. So I sat there. Boredom was not an issue then—that would come later.

The caregiver, when she arrived (two hours late), turned out to be an apologetic alcoholic. I could smell her liquored-up breath as soon as she walked in the door. *Great*, I thought, *the blind leading the blind*. Still, I was glad to have someone there, and she did have a rudimentary knowledge of how to take care of someone. Emphasis on the rudimentary.

At that point, I needed her to stay the night, because I needed my walker to, among other things, brush my teeth and comb my hair. I needn't have worried. Once she got me up, she went back to sleep for a while.

I wish I could say I sent her packing the second day. But I was very, very needy, so she stayed two weeks. When she finally did leave, her son had to come pick her up. For some reason (too many DUIs, maybe?) she didn't have a car. And she lived 75 miles away. In a big enough city that she should have had plenty of work where she lived. I guess the agency that sent her didn't ask too many questions. For instance, I had specified that whomever they sent *had to have a car*. Turns out she lied about that. And didn't mention the drinking, of course.

A word to the wise: you get what you pay for. I was concentrating on keeping prices low; and the caregiver agency had the best prices. But it turned out there was a reason. There followed a parade of the sorriest women you ever saw. One was obsessed with her appearance; the day she arrived, she gave herself a manicure right in front of me. Complete with glitter on her nails. There were other alcoholics, there were cell phone junkies who never even looked at me. I might as well have been a sick chimpanzee; all they did was talk on the phone. And get paid for it.

There was one woman who was so abusive I was afraid of her. She yelled at me often and was very strict about everything. I couldn't wait to see *that* one go. Unfortunately, you are at the mercy of people who need help themselves. And do they ever resent taking care of someone else.

Which is why I could have cried with happiness when Delia came along. She was private; you could only get her through word of mouth, which I did. Her hourly rate was higher than the agency's, but not that much higher. At that point, I didn't care what I paid. I just wanted to be treated like a human being. A sick one, to be sure, but a human nonetheless.

It was a few months into my recovery. I still hadn't been alone, and Delia took up residence in the guest bedroom. I was delighted to have her there, although paying for care 24/7 was depleting my bank account. Why don't politicians care about this? It seems criminal to me.

Delia was great company; she regaled me with funny stories about her life. We watched TV together, went for walks (I was still using a walker); she read to me when I was too tired to read. She was a great cook. And I had still not been left alone for a minute.

Thank goodness my California brother mentioned that he thought I qualified for state disability. Delia knew about this. She was shocked that I wasn't getting regular checks already.

It turned out to be such a maze, and the state government was so unresponsive, that I ended up hiring a lawyer to do the whole thing. Turns out there is a special, and different, phone number for lawyers. He got me signed up, and Delia was not such a luxury. I collected enough from the state to pay half her hourly amount. Mind you, every state is different; some will not pay at all. People obsess about income taxes, but they never think about what the state will do (or not do) when you really need it. California was very good to me. Florida, where I now live, won't give anything. You need to take this into account when you are contemplating where to live next. Because you may not always be so healthy.

In the end, I had to cut Delia down to daytime only. She stayed beyond what I paid her for and was worried about me during the evenings. But how could I expect less from someone who sent an adult family member to take care of me on the infrequent occasions when she couldn't? (They were all as delightful as she was.)

I had to get used to being home alone from six in the evening to eight in the morning.

At first, I was terrified. You should have seen my night-stand. Crammed, and I mean crammed, with everything I might need. If I had another stroke, well, too bad. There were no emergency apps then, I was truly on my own. Unless I could reach someone on my cell phone before I blacked out.

Those who have a family member who is willing and able to take care of them when they need it are very, very lucky. And in the beginning, you need it all the time. I lasted a year and a half before I started spending the evening and overnight by myself.

STROKES
CAN BE
CHARMING

What? There's nothing charming about having a stroke. Nothing!

That's what I thought, too. And it's all too easy to think that, as you galumph along, swaying and swerving, not moving too fast because you don't have enough balance. I *still* tend to go in the same direction without control, only now I can just about stop myself. Just.

But the other day a friend told me someone who encountered me recently thought I was from France. And this isn't the first time. I've been told on several occasions that I have a European accent. Eastern Europe some people think, others assume I'm from Western Europe.

Folks, I am battling aphasia. But...my speech therapist, early on, told me I would end up with a European accent. I dismissed that, thinking it could not possibly be true. And yet, here it is. To some, I sound European.

I'll take it. If that's the price I have to pay, so be it. A European accent is much better than a drunken slur. It's *charming*.

If you think of yourself this way, it's easier to have had a stroke. You are not broken. You are *different*.

Sure, you walk funny. Maybe you're still in a wheelchair. You talk funny, too. Until you get better, this is what you have to work with. Try to make it advantageous. Be funny.

Be charming. People will like you in spite of your stroke. Let them know that this disability has not stopped you. No, Sirree.

Who do you admire most? People in wheelchairs who nevertheless can break dance? Or rock climb? Those who, despite their disability and perhaps great age, enjoy listening to jazz and can make a great omelet?

I believe that if you hide in your house, ashamed of the things you can no longer do, you don't get much sympathy. Remember Mr. Rochester of the book *Jane Eyre*? He kept his crazed wife locked in the attic. Who thinks of her? I know people who have had strokes who just don't go out. They're missing out on so much. Not to mention that no one finds them *charming*.

After a stroke, it may be hard to imagine anyone ever accepting you again, much less liking you. Yet you are just another person . . . one who's had a stroke. Probably lost some major abilities. That's not a jail sentence. It's a starting point.

Strokes are full of surprises. You may someday be able to do something you never thought you could do. I've surprised myself and the people around me.

Who knows, you may end up with a European accent.

My
Experience
with
Barre

After my move to the Central Coast of California, and my happy discovery that I could do yoga again, I moved to Florida. The yoga classes in Florida are all far away from home and early in the morning, and anyway no one is going to yoga class right now because of COVID-19. You can do it online, but that gets old. And, to be honest, nothing equals that group energy you get with a class. Not to mention the teacher noticing you're doing something wrong and correcting you.

So I let myself be dragged, by a woman I met while walking the dog, to a Barre class. Talk about a challenge! I am still in shock that I can get through a class.

Barre is fast. Barre is hard. Barre seems to concentrate on the major muscle groups. My quadriceps and glutes will never be the same. And when you've had a stroke, it seems impossible to do.

First, the speed. There is no way to comprehend this when nurses are having you walk slowly down the hallway, intravenous poles in tow. Someone holding onto you by your hospital gown or pajamas. Walking to the end of the hall and back may feel like climbing Mount Everest, but it's nothing compared with how you feel when fast music with a driving beat gets turned on and you're surrounded by people *who can do this.*

In the beginning, I stumbled through each class like someone who never exercised before. I learned a lot. Like if I threw myself into it, I lost my balance. Except in rare instances, my arms could not coordinate with my legs. It was one or the other, but not both. I chose my legs.

In the beginning, I could not keep up. Five weeks or so into it, I still lose it sometimes, but mostly I can move with the class. This is a victory of sorts.

I'm relieved and shell shocked when the class is over. Do I like it? Not really. I kind of grit my teeth and am so happy when it's done with. I treat myself to an iced (this is Florida; it's hot) coffee when it's over. Now *that* I enjoy.

But . . . I get around with more confidence. I'm now aware of how everything is connected, so I know I have to strengthen my hips and quads to walk better. That right leg is gaining some control. So what if I run for the aspirin bottle as soon as I get home?

I consider it a major win that I can walk from the living room to the kitchen. I know that staying in my comfort zone won't get me anywhere. Remember when I said that you have to be willing to look like an idiot to make any progress? Unfortunately, that's as true after seven years as it is after one and a half. I *still* have to push myself after I've gone as far as I think I can go. There's no magic bullet (yet), there's only sweat.

So I'm taking Barre class. And sweating a lot. And moving too fast. And doing too much.

In the movie *Manu*, some guy who's had a terrible accident and whose body has taken quite a beating gets back into (incredible) shape partly by dragging tires on chains up and down an inclined ramp. When you watch him staggering beneath that weight and *carrying on*, a Barre class doesn't seem so bad.

In fact, when you think about it, which you'd often rather not, the people who recover *from anything* the best are usually athletes. They push and drive themselves relentlessly. You don't need to do what they do. You do need to take a Barre class. Or *something* that you think you can't do.

It's
All
a Blur

Writing this book has been, well—*instructive*. I've had to relive things I don't want to relive, think about things I don't want to think about. What were those early days like? Was it really so bad?

No, those early days were not bad. They were unspeakable. Unless you've had a stroke, you can never describe the confusion, the fear, the anger, the scrambling to make your life work. The doctors and nurses, the attendants, the hospitals, the therapists who become part of your daily routine. The sudden disability. The job loss. The sudden and complete *disruption*. Of everything.

On a scale of one to ten, your stress level suddenly reaches about twelve. No one can tell you what the future will bring because no one knows for sure what the future will bring, least of all you. I remember constantly asking, *will I be able to* ... walk, talk, write, all the basic things? No one could tell me.

The *only* thing the nurses had a definitive answer to was my double vision. They assured me it would go away in two weeks. Like clockwork, it disappeared in two weeks. It took much longer for me to be able to focus quickly and without a struggle. I felt, and probably looked, as if I were blind. I could see just fine, but I saw *everything*. TV helped a lot with that.

Now? Those early, immediately after year or two are a

blur. Then things smoothed out, acquired a rhythm. Recently, I had someone mention, in passing, that I was recovered. This was shocking, too. Because you think of yourself as this helpless thing long after you can do just about everything for yourself.

It's a good thing, I remind myself, that it's been so many years. That I've come so far. That I'm so *different* from that grim, sleepy scarecrow I was for the first few months. You tend to think you haven't come that far, but you have.

People no longer need to watch over you night and day. Doctors have dismissed you because they're no longer needed. You don't need help with everything. You have become . . . somewhat normal.

Now, few people guess that I've had a stroke. They know something is wrong with me, but they don't know what. Progress? I guess it is.

When I think back, I almost can't believe the nightmare I went through. Family and friends become a lifeline for you. Most of them won't be so vigilant after about six months. You haven't been deserted. You're just getting better.

I can remember a time when I didn't think life was worth living. Everything was so *hard*. Was I always going to struggle like this? Was it always going to be hard to turn off the TV at night? (Now they have remotes; they had them then, too, but now I actually use them.)

I still hesitate when I first get up and prepare myself to walk. But I'm no longer afraid. I still stagger to the bathroom in the middle of the night when I wake up and have to pee. But I do it—walk in the dark. Because I can.

They say that women would never have children if they knew how much pain was involved. I know women who stopped at one child because "I'm not going through that again." That's my only real fear about having another stroke—having to go through *that* again.

There were good things, too. I watched silly TV shows with my wonderful caregiver Delia, who was such a great companion. The first year, year and a half, I was saved from boredom because I slept so much. That's a constant refrain that I hear from stroke survivors—they sleep a lot. Your body has been through a massive attack; it stands to reason you're going to sleep it off for a while.

I have regained much of my old energy, but not 100%. That's okay. I haven't napped in the afternoon for, oh, a couple of years now. In fact, I've forgotten what it's like to get sleepy during the day.

I want to tell stroke patients who are near the beginning that it's going to get a lot better. *A lot*. It may be hard to envision it, but it will. Time marches on, and so does healing.

That's where it does pay to be young when you have a stroke. I've always thought, sometimes with ruefulness, that I'll reach my goals just in time to be old. For those who are young to begin with, in their 20s or 30s, they have the decade or so it's going to take to heal as much as they can. They may think, *I'm wasting my youth on this!* But as I know, you learn so much—much more than you would have if you hadn't had a stroke.

Would I do it all this way again? No. But I don't have that luxury. I've had a stroke and that's that. I don't like it, but there it is. You'll come around to that way of thinking, too.

Strokes have a way of teaching us about life and adversity. If you've survived, good for you: You may have a long road to recovery ahead of you, but you have a road.

OTHER
INJURIES

It may seem like adding insult to, yes, injury, but after the shock of the stroke wears off, you go back to being . . . as you were before. This means getting headaches, dealing with allergies, having other injuries. You think the stroke makes you immune, and for a while it does, but eventually you start sneezing again, and you realize your hay fever is back. This seems so unfair, but fortunately, after the stroke, life resumes. Suddenly all you wished for is there—the good and the bad.

Right now I'm dealing with an IT band issue. For those of you who luckily don't know, the IT band is the iliotibial tissue that runs along the outside of the leg from hip to knee. It hurts! I've had this before and thought it was gone forever, but here it is again. I've had to temporarily stop exercising. Again!

If you have a recurring ankle injury, or your elbow broke when you were a child and has never been the same since, the stroke only changes it temporarily, probably because after a stroke, you rest so much. But as soon as you start moving, or exercising regularly, the old injuries come back.

This is so disappointing. After all you've been through, you still have to deal with that elbow? In a nutshell, *yes*. The only saving grace—when people get together and start talking about their tendinitis, you can join in.

In a lot of ways, it feels good to be so normal that once again worrying about that ankle, or in my case, that outer hip feels good. Your head exploding has become a very old and half-forgotten issue. Because now it's your hip! Almost everyone can relate to that.

Hooray
for
YouTube

This is a shameless plug for a video I found on YouTube. Called *My Whale Eyes*, it's a very short film by James Robinson about how it feels to be different. And it's a diatribe on "normality" and the way people worship it.

James has a slight disability. His eyes go in different directions, and he can't really look at you straight on. It's called Strabismus, and he has the complications of also having Alternating Exotrobia and something called A.R.C. But it says a lot that his own brother doesn't really know anything about his condition. James's brother just laughs about it, and only knows that James has weird eyes.

I actually knew someone who had this condition, and it says something that I never asked her what was wrong with her eyes. That was before my stroke, not that it's any excuse. But now I would ask.

I think all stroke survivors should watch this video, because they can certainly relate. Some might be lucky enough to have made a full recovery and although they look "normal," they don't feel normal. And they're not. They know how mortal they are. Other people don't.

My Whale Eyes is so poignant, and it says so much. When you are "normal," you just don't pay attention to people who aren't. Then, one day, a stroke happens to you, and your whole perspective changes. For better or worse.

I don't have any answers about this, only more questions. You can draw your own conclusions, including why some disabilities seem to be more acceptable than others. Chew on that for a while.

Are We There Yet?

Children all ask this in the car. They are so impatient when it comes to traveling. Cars, planes, trains, all make them kick their feet (often on the back of the seat in front of them, where an irate person is sitting), and ask repeatedly, "Are we there yet?"

I had my eighth anniversary of my stroke a month ago. I used to celebrate; I don't see the need for celebrating any more. It's clear I have survived. The last three or four years have been pretty good, actually. I'm still making progress, although it is no longer by leaps and bounds. I don't jump out of bed in the morning, suddenly able to walk and talk. Still, here I am.

I have a theory. Over time, you lose your enthusiasm for getting better. You want it—oh, how you want it! Yet you realize, or at least I do, that the more you do, the closer you get to normal, the more people will leave you to doing just about everything. They haven't stopped caring. Far from it. But everyone has tons to do now (when did we get so busy?), and they are very relieved that you now can do so many more things on your own.

A family member of mine often says wistfully, "Everyone was so nice to me when I had cancer." That was over thirty years ago, and she still remembers it! The same is true of strokes. Everyone is so nice to you when you've had a stroke. People love to be helpful, and they have lots of patience for it for, say, the first four years. Then, well—they're ready to move on, and you'd better be, too. They won't do things for you forever.

In the last year, I've started to have moments—just moments—when I actually feel normal. I find this, not exhilarating, as you might imagine, but kind of scary. I imagine if you're one of the lucky ones who recovers fast, this feels triumphant. But if you've been handicapped for years, this is a very big change. One that takes some getting used to.

That little handicapped sign that I hang from my rearview mirror, for instance. I've always needed it, but now I need it less. I can walk longer distances, and I've started to not use my cane walking from parking lots into stores. Woohoo, that's progress!

Yet in the back of my mind, I worry about the day when the DMV and my doctor decide I don't really need it any more. I can park anywhere and walk. This sounds wonderful, but maybe it isn't so wonderful. It means that, in many cases, I have to park pretty far away and walk a long distance. *Just like most people do without thinking.*

I still remember a time when I thought nothing of parking in downtown Berkeley and walking everywhere in town from then on. I had to feed the meter and remember where and when I parked, because I only had so much time before I either had to move my car or feed the meter again. Those days are going to come back. Now it's even more urgent, because I have to put a slip of paper on my dash saying when I have to buy another ticket...or else.

I may be delighted when I have to do this again. But there'll be a period of adjustment.

Maybe a stroke survivor is not getting better because in the back of their mind, they know that, although life will get much better in some ways, it will get worse in others. They're not making it up—it's true. At least, they're not the only ones who feel this way.

Couple that with the lack of drive to do therapy every

day, and it's no wonder people get stuck. The incentive just isn't there.

After eight years, I've learned very well how to compensate for being weak and shaky on one side. Or how to avoid doing things that I know I can't do. I could easily spend the rest of my life this way. But—I really do want to keep making progress. If I get better in increments, so be it.

I'm not there yet. But someday I will be.

Made in the USA
Coppell, TX
12 February 2023

12694932R00152